Co

Pru *and* Family

Acknowledgements

I would like to thank my wife Liz for her encouragement and for pushing me to both write and finish this story. Also to her late mother for financing its production.

Thanks also to Ann Broadfield for typing the manuscript, to Steve Powell for his advice and help and to Buddug Roberts for her support.

I knew what the honourable Pru should look like but could not do the artwork myself – so it's thanks to our good friend Pom Instance, whose dogs Drake and Bentley are a big part of the story, for producing the front cover.

Finally a big thank you to the stars of the book - our three Labradors Pru, Paddy and Mollie and also to Drake and the other puppies who go to make up *Pru and Family*.

For Liz

CHAPTER ONE

PRU

For as long as anyone could remember Pru had lived at The Hall. She was really the Honourable Prudence but was known by all the family as Pru. She came from a long and noble Irish family and had been married to Drake for many years.

Drake, or Admiral Drake to give him his full title, was from a seafaring family and would be away from home for many months at sea. He would leave The Hall and the village of Drakeshead-on-Sea where they lived for long periods of time on his boat. Drake would arrive back with his Admiral's hat on wearing his full naval uniform with his brass buttons shining, and was never far from the telescope that he kept for looking out to sea. So Pru spent quite a lot of time on her own at The Hall, but she was well known and respected around the village.

Pru was always elegantly dressed and was frequently seen in the village wearing her tweeds and pearls and always looking her best. Outside The Hall Pru's car was parked as usual, a green convertible Mercedes sports car with her own personalised number plate, PRU 1.

The Hall was a large imposing building in the centre of the village of Drakeshead-on-Sea. There was a grand entrance hall with rooms leading off it and a large staircase going upwards. Halfway up the stairs were double doors opening out onto a balcony, the stairs then led on to two floors with bedrooms above. There were big trees in front and behind The Hall, which was just down the road from the parish church, St. Bernard's, with its clock and tall spire. On top of the spire was a little cockerel weather vane which spun around and pointed in the direction that the wind was blowing.

In the centre of the village was the village green with a little wishing well, and just at the side of this was the village pub, "The Two Collies"' with its thatched roof. This was the village of Drakeshead-on-Sea.

The village nestled up to the coast and was well suited for Drake and his seafaring expeditions. There were boats bobbing up and down in the harbour and a little lighthouse warning them of the dangers of the rocks nearby. Surrounding the village there were fields leading up to the big mountains, with a winding road over the hills which led down the other side to the county town of Foldingham.

Pru was pleased that all her family were around her in the village now. The church just down the road, St. Bernard's, was where her son Murphy was the vicar. The Reverend Murphy lived in the house next door to the church. Murphy always wore a little dog collar, a white collar back to front, and a dark suit. He was always very serious these days and this is not at all how he had been in the past. Murphy was just one of seven of Pru's family all of whom live around the village now.

Just down the road from the church there is a row of shops, the first one of which is a florist shop which is known as 'Bentley's Bloomers' where another of Pru's sons, Bentley, sells flowers and plants. Bentley was always the artistic one of the family, and could be seen around the village carrying large bunches of gladioli or other flowers, and he could toss a flower arrangement together in seconds. Once a week a fresh delivery would arrive from Holland for Bentley's shop and this would be brought over by the Dutch twins, Dirk and Derek. They arrived in their van every week and on the side of the van it says simply 'Dirk and Derek Dutch Florists.'

Everyone thought it strange when they first arrived from Holland as they both wore clogs on their feet and white overalls. One twin had 'Dirk' written on his chest and the other had 'Derek' written on his, otherwise it would be totally impossible to tell one from the other. Now they are part of the village life, and everyone expects to see them every week. Bentley always wears brightly coloured shirts in pinks and yellows, with flowery ties and brightly coloured suits, which match all the colourful flowers he sells in his shop.

Next door to him his brother, Tebor, runs a small electrical shop, and drives around sorting out all the repairs in the village in his blue truck with 'Tebor's Electrics' on the side of it. Tebor always seems very happy. He wears blue overalls to work and when his van passes by you he can be heard whistling a happy little tune.

One of the other brothers, Bramley, is the local policeman, and the village police station is also on the edge of the village green. Bramley either goes around the village on his bicycle, or he can be seen 'walking the beat.' He goes around every night with his torch checking the shops and making sure everything is safe and all secure. Last thing at night he always walks past The Hall to make sure that his mother is safe for the night before settling down himself for the evening. He always wears his policeman's uniform with pride, and his shoes are so well polished that everyone says they can see their faces in them. All he had ever wanted to do since he was a young puppy was to be a policeman.

That is four of the boys. What of their sisters? Well sister Mollie is the local doctor. Her surgery is past the shops. Every morning and every evening Mollie holds a surgery for anyone who is not well to come along to. At work she always wears a white coat and has a stethoscope around her neck. Mollie lives in a little house behind the surgery so that she is always there when anyone needs her if there is a problem in the village.

The other sister Nicole runs the local golf club which is on the edge of the village. Nicole was once a dancer on the stage but has now given this up and has come back home to Drakeshead. She is usually seen in golfing skirts or trousers with checked patterns on them, and a hat on her head when she is playing golf because of her famous flowing red hair, which needs to be kept in place. The golf club is a popular place and the family often gather there on a Sunday for their lunch.

Finally the seventh of the children in the family and the oldest of the children is Paddy, or Paddy the farmer as he is known. Paddy always wanted to be a farmer, and he runs his farm on the outskirts of the village and lives in the big farmhouse. Paddy can often be seen working in the fields driving his tractor with his flat cap on his head and wearing his big warm tweed suit. Paddy also likes to fly his aeroplane and has a small runway on one of the fields on the farm. He and his sister Mollie can often be seen taking off in the plane. Mollie and Paddy had always been close right from when they were born and they always seemed to have a special friendship.

So this is Pru's family, all of them living and working around the village of Drakeshead-on-Sea. Now that the family have grown up and are all working and living in the village Pru and Drake live on their own at The Hall. In the early days before the puppies were born Pru spent long months alone at The Hall whilst Drake was away at sea.

Pru often sits in the hallway in her large pink reclining chair. It had always been her chair and carries many memories for her. On this day she sat thinking how comfortable it was in the village with all her family around her. She thought how the village had been, how the village was, and how it always would be. She thought of what memories this chair carried for her and she settled down and drifted off to sleep.

CHAPTER TWO

IN THE BEGINNING

In the early days at The Hall Pru was on her own a lot whilst Drake was away at sea. She loved to curl up in her old pink reclining chair in the hallway and relax and go to sleep.

One day as she was drifting off to sleep she was surprised to find her chair rising slowly and twisting round and round. As she opened her eyes and suddenly looked up, she saw the large French windows halfway up the stairs open wide, and the chair continued to rise from the floor. It gently spun around and took her through the open windows and upwards into the air towards the blue sky outside.

First it rose over the trees and the garden and over towards the church at Drakeshead with the cockerel weather vane on top. The cockerel spun around with surprise seeing her in the chair, and roared, 'cock-a-doodle-do,' at Pru. She gave the cockerel a spin with the flick of her tail and he spun round again three times. The chair climbed higher and higher and Pru sat bolt upright and stared down at the village of Drakeshead below.

How wonderful it looked. She had never seen it from this height before. It was all laid out in a patchwork pattern and she could see The Hall, the church and the village green with its little pond, and the row of shops coming down from the vicarage. The coastline was quite clear to her and she could see the boats coming and going in the harbour and the rolling fields of the farms and the mountains in the distance.

Pru marvelled at these sights below her, not knowing that such things were possible. Leaning forward to get a better view she peered down towards the church and almost fell off the chair. For a moment she felt frightened but she knew she would be safe in her old chair and that it would not let her down. The chair continued to rise. She realised she was leaving the village behind and the chair was taking her over the mountains at the edge of the village. The chair rose higher and higher and Pru held on for fear of falling. She knew that the county town of Foldingham was beyond the mountains and she could see the tall spire of the cathedral in the distance.

As she came close she could see the bishop, Bishop Rodney, a tall handsome chocolate Labrador dressed in purple, coming out of the cathedral. She crouched down in her chair as she did not want him to see her, but she needn't have worried because he did not look up. The service at the cathedral was over and everyone was coming out through the main doors. Pru was afraid someone would see her and recognise her, but the chair was not going to let that happen and took her higher over Foldingham and into the open country.

Pru could hear the sound of flapping wings and was surprised to see a bird landing on the arm of the chair. It was Percy the pigeon who had been living at The Hall for years and was an old friend of the family.

'What are you doing up here Pru?' he asked. 'This is my world, we don't see Labradors up here very often.'

Pru put her finger up to her lips, 'Percy, this will be our little secret there is no point in telling anyone in Drakeshead about what you have seen.'

'Don't worry Pru, your secret is safe with me but hadn't you better be getting home soon? It's nearly four o'clock and tea will be served at The Hall and you will be missed.'

Pru shook her head in disbelief, where had the time gone? The chair spun around and moved off towards Drakeshead, passing over the mountain range and leaving the tall spire of Foldingham cathedral in the distance.

Soon she was flying over the familiar landmarks of her own village. The chair moved in through the open windows and passed down into the hall and came to rest in its usual spot opposite the big grandfather clock. Pru shook herself and yawned as the clock struck four o'clock. Time for tea and everything was as before.

She headed off to the drawing room where tea and scones awaited her. That is the ways things had always been at The Hall and in the village and that is the way they always would be.

CHAPTER THREE

ARRIVAL OF THE PUPPIES

Pru had many adventures in her big armchair and enjoyed going out from The Hall and we will come back to these in the future.

One afternoon Pru was sitting in her big pink armchair in the hallway, thinking back to some of these adventures when her mind wandered to the puppies. How things had changed over the years, she thought, since the little ones were born. Seven little treasures, five boys and two girls.

On the first night they lay there sleeping, 'five black and two yellow', and she and Drake sat over them and smiled contentedly at each other. Two proud parents of seven perfect little puppies. The yellow ones, a boy and a girl, they called Paddy and Nicole, the other five black ones, four boys and a girl were christened Bentley, Murphy, Tebor, Bramley and of course little Mollie.

When the puppies were born nothing seemed strange for the first day as everyone was so excited. Pru and Drake watched closely over them. Pru noticed something odd however in the small black girl, the one they called Mollie. She was born with her eyes open, and from the first day she continually went over to the corner of their bed in the hallway, and looked up towards the bright lights shining in through the French windows at the top of the stairs. She was not alone standing there because her little white brother called Paddy was always with her. His eyes were not open, but he had both ears pricked up and also like Mollie he looked towards the bright light pouring in from the French windows. The days went by and the puppies grew larger and more active. Pru and Drake stood over them and wondered why these two were so different from the rest.

In the days to come Pru was to find out, and it would be her secret to share only with Paddy and Mollie. About four weeks after the puppies were born Pru was watching over them in the hallway. As usual Paddy and Mollie were apart from the others and they had fallen asleep looking up towards the big bright light. The other four brothers and sister were curled up in a bundle all snoring loudly. Pru was tired because she had had a lot of sleepless nights watching over the little ones and Drake had been away for a few days. The puppies looked peaceful and safe, so she got up on her old faithful armchair in the hallway and curled up.

Soon her eyes were closing and she was drifting off to sleep. As she dozed off, she felt the chair rising up out of the hallway and up towards the open French windows in the hall. She was frightened to be leaving the puppies behind and looked down, but she could not stop the chair taking her up further. There was a very bright light ahead and her eyes opened up wide to see where she was going. Unlike previous trips in the chair she did not go out over the church and the village, but rose higher and higher towards the white light that was getting brighter and brighter. She looked back and could no longer see the village behind her.

Where was she going she wondered? She was so worried she had left the little ones on their own and she had no idea what was ahead of her. As she rose higher and higher the white mists in front of her disappeared and she started to see a clear image. As she got nearer she could see the purest white Labrador's head appearing in front of her. She realised as she got closer this must be Albos, as she had heard talk of him, but no one had ever seen him before. Albos was one of those known as a Goddog. Pru had heard that he existed but had never met him. She stared in amazement at the sheer size and brightness of this pure white Labrador's head.

He smiled lovingly at her, 'Don't be afraid Pru, I have

brought you here to explain certain mysteries to you. You will by now have noticed that two of your little puppies are different to the others, the ones you have called Paddy and Mollie.'

Pru nodded, she didn't know what to say.

'These two puppies have been chosen to have special powers to help them as they grow, so that with your help they can fight evil in the world. You must promise me Pru that you will keep these secrets to yourself and not even share them with the rest of the family or the village. Do you agree?'

What could Pru answer, she didn't know what was coming next and so she simply nodded in agreement. Albos looked at her and smiled again reassuringly.

'Pru, you remember Mollie was born with her eyes open. She has the power of sight ten times that of any other dog. She can see through walls and over long distances and can see just as well in the dark. Her big brother, the one you call Paddy, has the power of hearing ten times stronger than any other dog. Both Mollie and Paddy have other extra strengths so that they can run faster than any other dog and their powers will grow as they grow older. They both know each other's strengths and will work together to use them for good. None of the other puppies or their father will ever know of this. I trust all of this to you Pru. The puppies must be brought up in the village in the usual way. They must take normal jobs, and you must train them in years to come to use these powers to help them and help others.'

Pru was looking anxious at all she had learnt and what she must do. She looked at Albos and said, 'What if questions are asked or anyone guesses the truth?'

'Remember Pru only you and Paddy and Mollie know the truth. If anyone asks questions you simply tell them to look up at the bright light in the sky and the whole episode will be forgotten and life will go on as usual. Do you understand Pru?'

Pru wasn't sure that she had taken all this in, but nodded to

Albos in agreement.

'I will talk to you again about this in the future,' said Albos, 'and I will send help to teach Paddy and Mollie how to make the most of their powers.' Albos looked at her finally with a smile again and said, 'Now run along Pru, you have work to do. Those little puppies of yours will be waking up and will need feeding.'

At that the bright light started to fade and Albos' image started to grow dim. Pru's chair started to slowly rotate back towards earth. Suddenly she could see the village below and the little shops, the village green and finally The Hall. The chair slowly moved in through the French windows and she could see Paddy and Mollie apart from the other puppies. They were awake with their heads on their paws looking directly at her and giving her a knowing smile. Paddy looked up towards her and winked his right eye as the chair moved down through the hall.

Pru thought, they know don't they? They know exactly what is ahead of them. The chair came down and landed in the hallway back in its normal place. Pru looked around and saw that all the puppies were gradually waking up wagging their tails frantically and wanting their lunch and afterwards they would want a story told to them. That is the way it was every day at The Hall with the puppies when they were young.

CHAPTER FOUR

PRU CONSIDERS
THE PUPPIES' EDUCATION

The puppies grew rapidly and got into all sorts of mischief. Pru came in one day to find them taking turns to slide down the banisters in the hall and landing on an old bean bag which Paddy and Mollie had dragged across and put in place for them. These two always looked after the other ones and with Mollie's sense of sight and Paddy's sense of hearing they kept them out of all kinds of danger.

Pru looked at them all there in the hall and was very proud of them. What fine puppies, she thought. It was time to take the little ones out around the village and show them off to the neighbours. The village was very small. In those days there was The Hall of course and a few small farms dotted around the neighbourhood. The village green was there with its duck pond, the church with its tall spire and the cockerel weather vane on top, the old thatched roof pub called "The Two Collies" and a few cottages dotted around the edge.

Pru told the puppies that they were going out in the car, and they all had to be very good and sit still, and in particular no jumping out of the car as this was extremely dangerous. They all looked very solemn but were obviously very excited at this new adventure. Little Murphy was trembling as he knew he would find it very difficult to be still and be good at the same time.

They all followed Pru out through the big front door where Pru's car was waiting in the drive. They hadn't seen the car before and there in front of them was the lime green Mercedes sports car with the roof down. Paddy was studying the number plate PRU 1 and although he couldn't read yet he knew it looked familiar.

'Come on then, let's all get in,' said Pru. 'First Bentley, Tebor, Bramley, Murphy and Nicole I want you all to get into the back.' The front seat was pulled forward and one by one they piled in. 'Now all sit quietly and Murphy,' she said turning to him directly, 'don't even think about jumping out. Now Mollie and Paddy come on to the front seat next to me.' They all climbed in and Pru got in and put her headscarf around her head. Then she started the car which roared with approval as they raced down the drive.

Pru had never mastered driving the car at any other speed than very fast. The puppies were all thrown back in their seats as the car zoomed away.

'Hold tight puppies, we're off!'

She sped off from The Hall past the church with the vicarage next door. The church of St. Bernard's had been in the village as long as The Hall and it was Pru's ancestor Moll Doggins who had built it and the family had supported it ever since.

The old vicar, The Reverend Chumley was in his garden pottering around. He was dressed up in a straw hat and carried a little basket because he had been looking after his bees. Pru pulled the car up and he waved and came across to the car to say 'hello.' The Reverend Chumley was a wise old spaniel who wore round rimless glasses and walked in a slow deliberate way in keeping with his advanced age. Pru looked at him and thought, he is not going to be able to manage this job for many more years. She remembered how long and slow his sermons had become. She would have to look in years to come for someone younger to take over at the church.

The Reverend Chumley came up to the car and touched the brim of his straw hat. 'Good day m'lady fine day.' He looked the puppies over and said, 'Fine family of puppies m'lady to be sure.'

'Thank you Chumley,' said Pru. 'Glorious day for their first outing,' she added looking up at the sunshine all over the village. 'Are you just tending your bees Chumley? I will have some more of that fine honey from you again when it's ready. I am sure the puppies would love some on their breakfast biscuits.'

'There will be some for you just as soon as it's ready m'lady.'

'Thank you Chumley, we are doing a tour of the village so we must get on.'

The car lurched forward and again the puppies were thrown back in their seats as Pru drove on. They went around the side of the village green and past the duck pond. Murphy saw the ducks and wanted to jump out of the car and chase them and was about to move when Pru turned towards him and shouted, 'Don't even think of it Murphy,' and he stopped instantly.

At the far side of the village green was the thatched roof pub "The Two Collies". Mrs Collie was on the doorstep cleaning the big brass door knocker when Pru pulled up outside and Mrs Collie came across to the car to look at the family.

'Oh my! Your ladyship, aren't they just gorgeous. You must be very proud.'

Pru smiled in reply and said, 'Both the Admiral and myself are very proud of them Mrs Collie.'

'How is the Admiral?' asked Mrs Collie.

'He has been away at sea a long time on this trip, and it's sad because he is missing the puppies growing up, but he will be home soon and we are all looking forward to that aren't we puppies?'

The puppies were all excited at the thought of their father returning. They said goodbye to Mrs Collie and then drove on around the village past the little cottages and farms, and Pru waved at everyone they passed.

Time was moving on and it was getting towards lunchtime, so they headed back to The Hall. They all tumbled out of the car and up the steps back into the hallway. They had some lunch and were soon asleep and all dreaming of the new and exciting things they had seen today. Pru looked at them asleep in the hall and smiled at the sight of Paddy and Mollie side by side with their little heads on their paws, pointing in the direction of the window on the stairs as usual. The other five had leapt onto the old bean bag. They were a jumble of heads and tails and legs and all snoring and twitching as they dreamed heavily.

Pru wondered what was to become of them all in the future but first they would all have to start school. She hadn't yet taken them past the little school in the village on their outings. It was down the lane between The Hall and the church and she thought she would take them there another day. Pru jumped up onto her old familiar pink chair. As she sat there she noticed the puppies had chewed part of the pink seat although fortunately not much damage had been done, but she must speak to them about it. She wasn't having any damage done to her favourite chair.

She looked across at Paddy and Mollie. What was to become of them, she hadn't thought much of their future since Albos had told of her of their special powers. He had said that she was to teach them how to use these special powers, but how, she didn't know what their powers were apart from Mollie's special sense of sight and Paddy's sense of hearing. No doubt she would learn in the days to come.

She sat back in her chair and drifted off to sleep. She hadn't been asleep long when she woke with a start as the chair started to rise up into the air and slowly turned around and around. The chair reached the top of the stairs and the big French windows flew open. She looked down at the puppies fast asleep below. She wasn't so concerned about leaving them this time as she knew they were much older now. The chair took her out of the house and over the church. Pru passed the cockerel on the church spire, which spun around in amazement and crowed at her as she passed. She flicked it with her paw and it spun round three times again.

Off up and up she went leaving the village far behind her. The little houses and farms were just specks in the distance and then she couldn't see them at all. As the chair moved up into the clouds, the light got brighter and brighter and then there was such a white light that Pru had to cover her eyes with her paws.

She then heard a soft gentle voice saying, 'Open your eyes Pru you won't be harmed.' When she did there was that pure white-faced Labrador Albos ahead of her. This time he was sitting on a large white chair and said to her, 'Come over to me Pru.' Pru sat on the edge of her chair afraid to step off onto the clouds.

'Don't worry Pru you can walk over with no problem.'

She stepped off carefully and to her surprise was able to leave the chair and walk over to Albos, and when she got up close she could see that he was sitting on a gold throne. The mists were all swirling around the big gold chair. There was another smaller gold chair opposite him and he beckoned Pru to sit on it, which she did. She thought to herself how much safer she felt when she was on a chair again rather than walking on the clouds.

Albos turned across to her and said, 'Do you remember all I told you when we met last time Pru about the two puppies you call Paddy and Mollie. I told you that they will grow up to be very special and will have special powers and how I want you to bring them up to know how to make the most of these powers?'

Pru nodded and said she remembered, but she didn't know how she could do all this alone.

'You won't be alone Pru, I shall send my faithful manservant, Methuselah to help you. He is a very old Chinese hound who has a lot of wisdom and knows what Paddy and Mollie need to be taught.'

'But how will I know him when he arrives at The Hall?' Pru asked.

'That's easy,' said Albos. 'You'll know him when he arrives. It won't be for a little while and it may not be as you expect, but I think you'll know when the time approaches. I will send him to you and by day he will work around the house and by night he will be Methuselah who will help with the education of Paddy and Mollie.'

Pru looked worried, 'But Drake is away and not due home yet. I will have to tell him how I need more help around the house. I don't even know where his boat is. We are secretly very concerned because it's a long time since we have heard from him and I dare not tell the puppies that I am worried.'

Albos smiled at her, 'Don't worry Pru I will show you where he is.' He reached down with his big white paw and cleared a square opening in the clouds. Far below on the water Pru could see Drake's little boat drifting along on a very calm, still sea. 'We must bring him home quicker mustn't we Pru?' Albos bent forward and blew through the hole in the clouds and Pru could see the little boat gathering speed.

'There we are Pru,' said Albos. 'Drake will be home with you quite soon and then you can talk to him about help around the house and I will send someone to you. But you had better get home now as your puppies will need feeding, and you have work to do.'

Pru carefully got off her gold chair and walked across the clouds again to her old familiar pink chair, which started to move back down towards the earth, twisting slowly. The clouds thickened above her and she lost sight of Albos. She was soon down over the village again and she could see The Hall. She came down past the church and the cockerel crowed at her as she went past. Then she slipped in through the French windows and the chair landed down in the hallway just as the puppies were all waking up and ready for their lunch.

CHAPTER FIVE

MOLL DOGGINS AND THE SQUIRMITS

As the puppies were growing up Pru would tell them stories of the "old days" in the village. She would sit on her old pink chair in the hallway and the puppies would gather around her to listen. Each puppy had his or her own seat and each one was a different colour. Paddy and Mollie always sat together at the right hand side of their mother, Paddy in his little green chair and Mollie in her little yellow chair, both chairs had their names on the back of them.

They always sat next to each other so they could look up at the big window and the light at the top of the stairs. The other five, Bentley, Nicole (who was known as Toffee by all the family because her coat was the colour of toffee), Bramley, Tebor and Murphy each had their own little chairs, purple, orange, red, blue and black. When it was time for a story they all pulled their chairs forward and sat listening. There were lots of stories Pru told them about the "old days" in the village, but the one they always wanted to hear was the one about Moll Doggins and the Squirmits.

They would all sit in their chairs with their tails wagging, begging, 'Please Mum, tell us the story about the Squirmits again, please, please please.'

Pru usually gave in as it was easier in the end. She usually made it seem that she wasn't going to tell them a story, and would say, 'No, let's have a different one today,' but the puppies weren't having it and would look very sad. After some time Pru would give in and say, 'Oh all right then, so it's the Squirmit story again, you win puppies.'

They would all smile and wag their tails. Pru had told the

story of Moll Doggins and the Squirmits so many times, but still they got excited every time she told it. When the excitement died down and they were all sitting quietly, she began her story. 'A long time ago in the village there were very few houses, just a few cottages and farms, there were no shops and life was very simple. There was the church and of course there was The Hall. There always was The Hall, puppies, and there always will be The Hall.'

They all got very excited wagging their tails and pulling their little chairs nearer to get closer to their mother and to hear the story. 'In those days in "olden times" Moll Doggins, your great, great, great great, oh puppies, I don't know how many great greats grandmother, lived here alone at The Hall. She was a very old and very wise Labrador but she was also very frightened. Frightened? I hear you all say, how could Moll Doggins be frightened of anything living in this big old house. Oh puppies, in those days all that long time ago, she was frightened of the Squirmits.'

Having heard the story so many times before little Moll put her paws over her ears at this stage as she didn't want to hear any more.

Pru said, 'Come on Mollie, you know it will be all right in the end.' At this point Mollie went back to listening again but with one eye on Paddy her big brother because she knew that he would look after her if anything went wrong.

Paddy looked back giving her a knowing smile, putting his little paw on hers and whispering in her ear, 'It'll be all right Moll, Mum's right, no harm comes to anyone.'

Pru continued, 'Now, where was I?' Her half-moon glasses were balanced on the end of her nose as if she had to read the story from a book. 'Oh yes, the Squirmits, well Moll Doggins was always afraid that the Squirmits would come. Who were the Squirmits you may ask? Well they looked like something between a squirrel, a mouse and a rabbit. They had two tails, one big bushy one which came right up above their heads, and one long thin one which hung over their right arms and reached down to the floor. hey had long floppy ears, and they could run very fast and climb walls, and were able to fly through the air from tree to tree, and house to house. What did they do? They ate and ate. They ate anything they came across, cheese, wood, chocolate, anything, but they really loved strawberry jam. They would do anything to get strawberry jam, literally anything. Moll Doggins also loved her strawberry jam, and at four o'clock every afternoon tea was served at the strike of the big clock in the hallway.'

Pru looked over to the big clock and the puppies all turned around to look. 'That's right it is the same clock we still have today, and when afternoon tea was served at The Hall the best silver teapot was used and Moll Doggins had sandwiches and scones and always strawberry jam, bowls and bowls of strawberry jam. The Squirmits had not only two tails, but also had brilliant noses and could smell strawberry jam from miles and miles away, and would run as fast as they could in search of it.

One day whilst Moll Doggins was having her afternoon tea, served to her by her faithful butler Gomez, a lovely Spanish chinchilla, who had been with Moll for as long as she could remember, there was a large rattling noise at the doors and the windows, and the next thing she knew was that the house seemed to be full of Squirmits, rushing around emptying the strawberry jam pots. The house was full of them, and there in the middle of the drawing room was their leader, Squire Squirmit. He stood taller than the others and wore a black patch over his left eye. He was eating the last of the scones, which were dripping with strawberry jam, and was laughing with jam running down either side of his mouth. He laughed loudly at poor Moll who was hiding behind her chair with Gomez at her side. Moll had had enough; she was not putting up with this any more, and jumped up onto her chair and stood to her full height. Gomez looked worried and stayed at her side trembling. "Squire Squirmit, I will not tolerate you coming into my house and stealing my strawberry jam. Never again will you do it, I will make sure of that." She knew she wasn't sure at this stage how she would stop him, but she knew this couldn't go on happening any longer. Squire Squirmit had strawberry jam sliding down the side of his mouth and he laughed a long deep laugh that echoed all around the house and could be heard all over the village. He looked at Moll and smiled at her. His left front tooth was missing and his lips were red with strawberry jam. "Now we've found you Moll Doggins, we will be back. Such fine strawberry jam." At that moment he grabbed his tail which was hanging over his right arm, and licked a large piece of strawberry jam off his tail where it had stuck. "Yes, such fine strawberry jam, the best in all of the county. Yes we will be back, we will be back." At that point the Squirmits all left, all chanting, "We will be back, we will be back," leaving poor Moll Doggins and Gomez alone.'

The puppies were all on the edge of their seats. 'What happened next, what happened next?' they cried as if they didn't know. They had heard the story so many times before.

Pru continued, 'The next day Moll Doggins woke up early. She was not going to be beaten by Squire Squirmit, and his gang so she made sure The Hall was Squirmit proof. She started off by having big bolts put on all the doors, and had shutters fixed to all the upstairs windows. The doors downstairs had big iron bars to make them secure and the shutters to the upstairs windows were also locked. Moll Doggins thought of everything. She knew the Squirmits could eat their way through wood, so all the doors and shutters were lined with metal on the outside. She wasn't taking any chances. On the downstairs windows Moll had big shutters that pulled up from the floor and had big brass keys to lock them. On each shutter

Moll had a brass bell attached, which would ring if anyone touched them or tried to open the shutters. When Moll finally thought The Hall was safe she had a large brass bell put in the top of the chimneys, with a cord leading to downstairs so she could ring the bell to let everyone know if there were ever Squirmits about. Well Moll was prepared now and no Squirmit would ever break into The Hall again and so they never did. Moll regularly ate her strawberry jam at four o'clock with her tea, and sometimes the brass bells on the shutters on the windows would ring, but no Squirmit ever got in and no Squirmit has got in since.'

It was all very quiet in The Hall and the puppies sat watching their mother. Mollie broke the silence, 'Will they ever come back?' she asked with a worried look on her face.

'We don't know Mollie,' said Pru, 'that is why we still have the big shutters and the large bell in the tall chimney. We don't know if they ever will come back.' Mollie trembled at the thought.

Paddy put his paw around her shoulder, 'Don't worry Moll, I'm here to protect you.'

'Don't you worry any of you puppies,' said Pru. 'As I said we still have the shutters to the windows and we still have the big bell, and of course that's why we never have strawberry jam in this house any more. So puppies if we are worried, what do we sing?'

All the puppies sat up in their chair at this point and started to sing their little rap song together, 'Watch out, watch out there's a Squirmit about.'

Watch out, watch out there's a Squirmit about.'

Be on your guard, be on your guard, don't be caught out, don't be caught out.'

Watch out, watch out, there's a Squirmit about.'

'That's enough puppies,' said Pru, covering her ears with her paws.

'Again, again they all shouted,' and so Pru gave in and they sang their little song once more. At that point they all broke up laughing, settled down, and all curled up and went to sleep. Mollie and Paddy lay down together looking up at the light in the hallway.

Mollie still looking worried turned to Paddy and said, 'Paddy will they come back again?'

'Who Mollie?'

'The Squirmits of course.'

'No Moll never, and if they do I will sort them out. You and me together, don't you worry.'

'Paddy?'

'Yes Moll what now?'

'Do you think I will ever go to sleep?' she asked as she lay tapping her paws.

'Sure Moll, now close your eyes and get some rest,' he replied and so off to sleep she went.

But Pru who looked over them all now asleep knew that one day the Squirmits could come back and she wasn't going to risk it, but she wouldn't let the puppies know her fears. She would keep the shutters locked and she would keep the bolts on the doors and the bells on the window and the big bell in the chimney, which would warn the village should the Squirmits ever return. But of course to be really safe then no strawberry jam would ever be served in The Hall.

Pru was thinking as she slipped off to sleep, of course they would never come back. Did old Moll Doggins ever see them anyway?' Then she had a sneaking little thought before she dropped off that perhaps one day they would come back, just possibly.

But that's the way it always had been in the village and that is the way it always would be.

CHAPTER SIX

DRAKE'S RETURN

As Albos had predicted, Drake arrived home much earlier than planned. A message was sent on ahead to say that their boat had had an unexpectedly good head wind, and would be arriving a week early. All preparations were made in the little harbour at Drakeshead. The day the boat was due a little brass band assembled and the entire village gathered at the quayside awaiting the arrival of the boat. Pru got the puppies up early that morning and got them ready to go down to meet their father's boat. Pru was taking "the big truck" as the puppies called it to fetch Drake home, as they would need the extra space.

Stubbings, The Hall maid, had been up from early morning preparing sandwiches and lemonade and the big picnic hamper was already in the back of "the truck". The puppies all stood in line in the hallway. Pru went along them one by one checking they were all at their best. She checked they had all washed behind their ears and all had a clean handkerchief in case they got a bit upset at the sight of their father's return.

When all was OK they filed down the steps and piled into "the truck". Although they were getting bigger there was still room for Mollie and Paddy to sit next to Pru in the front, and the other five to sit on the back seat. They headed off round the village and down towards the quay. The puppies turned and waved to Stubbings as she stood on the steps waving back her little chequered handkerchief.

When they reached the harbour there was already a crowd gathered and quite a party atmosphere. The band was playing seafaring tunes and there were little stalls set up by travelling dogs who were telling fortunes, and stalls where you could throw balls into bowls and win a goldfish. Pru stood at the quayside and asked the puppies to sit quietly for a moment. She got out her binoculars and scanned the horizon looking for the boat.

'I see it, I see it' she shrieked trying not to show her obvious excitement. Everyone gathered round and Pru handed out the little flags for all the young ones to wave. The local flag was a pair of crossed paws on a white background. The puppies thought this was heaven and were already waving their flags around in great excitement.

The boat gradually got nearer and nearer and became much larger. As it approached they could see the sailors on the deck and there was Admiral Drake at the helm of the boat. How splendid he looked, Pru thought. The puppies waved their flags and their tails so fast poor Mollie thought she was going to fall over. Pru put her paw on her shoulder to steady her.

The boat pulled up by the quay and tied up as the band played 'For He's a Jolly Good Fellow' and one by one the little sailors came off. Most of them lived in Foldingham and the surrounding county towns and the families had travelled long distances to greet them. Finally the last to leave the boat was Drake himself, who came down the gangplank to cheers from all on the quay. He came straight over to Pru and hugged her and gave her a kiss. Some of those watching that day may have noticed a tear in Pru's eye, but she wouldn't have admitted to such emotion.

Then one by one each of the puppies came up and sat on their father's knee and he hugged them, all that is except Murphy, who as usual had been distracted and was following around a very fat Corgi from the village with a large stick of candyfloss. All the puppies and Pru turned towards him having noticed he was missing and shouted together, 'Don't even think about it Murphy,' at which he came running and leapt into his father's arms for a hug.

Pru thought how nice, the family is all complete again. They all piled into "the truck" and Drake drove with Pru at his side and the puppies all climbed into the back, amidst sandwiches, lemonade and flags. There would be time to sort it all out later once they were home.

When they arrived back at The Hall dinner was waiting. There was so much to talk about. Each of the puppies wanted their turn telling their Dad what they had been doing since he went away. Drake was so patient thought Pru, he sat and listened to each of them one by one until finally it came to Murphy's turn. By this stage the others were getting very heavy-eyed, the excitement of the day had been too much for them and they were all yawning. Murphy got up onto Drake's knee and looked sad and tired.

'And what have you been up to my little friend whilst I have been away?' Murphy looked very seriously at his Dad and sadly said, 'Nothing Dad they won't let me do anything I want to do.'

Drake knew this wasn't true but it was late and everyone was tired now. 'Don't worry my little one, we'll make sure you have a good time now I am home,' he replied but at this point they were all snoring loudly. Pru and Drake sat together for some time before going to bed.

'It's so good to have you home Drake, it's not easy now with the little ones they are into everything, and they run circles around Stubbings.'

'Christmas is coming up,' said Drake 'and we will have a wonderful time together. I don't need to go to sea again for a long time.' He thumbed through the pile of post that was on the old silver tray waiting for him. 'I see the bills keep coming in. Oh what's this one it has a Foldingham post mark?'

Drake opened the envelope and pulled out a crisp white card. 'It's an invitation for all of us from Rodney, Bishop of Foldingham, to go to the cathedral for a carol service next week. Shall we go and take the puppies? It would be a great start to Christmas.'

'Oh yes let's,' said Pru, 'the puppies have never been out of the village, and Christmas carols at the cathedral will really excite them.'

'Right I'll let Rodney know tomorrow, we haven't seen him for years. Anything else much happened Pru whilst I was away that I should know about?'

'Not much really, life at The Hall is as it always was and life in the village never changes.' Pru thought how she would love to tell Drake about Paddy and Mollie, and about Albos, but she knew she couldn't.

'Well,' replied Drake that is the way it always has been at The Hall and that is the way it always will be.'

They both yawned and took their mugs of cocoa and headed up the stairs to bed.

CHAPTER SEVEN

THE CAROL SERVICE

The Sunday for the carol service came around quickly. Everyone was told to be on their best behaviour and that they must be very quiet during the service. It was a big adventure as they had never been over the mountain and into Foldingham and they didn't know what a cathedral was or looked like. Pru explained that it was a very large church and it would be full tonight for the carols.

'Will the Reverend Chumley be there?' asked Bentley looking very serious.

'No,' said Pru, 'the service will be taken by Bishop Rodney. He will be all dressed up in purple and he will walk with a very large stick.'

They were going to go in "the truck" and they all piled in. Drake was driving and Pru sat in the front next to him. The car soon headed out of the village and started to wind around the mountain road. Drakeshead soon became a small spot in the distance. They went over the top of the mountains, and the puppies were excited to see the spire of the cathedral in Foldingham ahead of them.

As they got closer and closer to the cathedral they soon came up outside and parked up. Pru gave them their last instructions to be good in church and said that they would all get treats on the way home.

'That includes you Murphy. No barking during the sermon, however long it goes on.'

The other six turned to him and wagged a paw, 'Don't even think of it Murphy,' they all said.

Why do they always pick on me because I am the smallest, thought Murphy. One day I will get my own back on them, just you see.

Drake and Pru led the way into the large cathedral and the puppies followed behind. When they went through the big doors they could see that most of the pews were full. Mollie was quite frightened by it all and looked up into the darkness. The roof was so high that she could barely see it. Paddy could tell she didn't like it, and as usual he always looked after her and cared for her, and put his big paw around her shoulder and said, 'Don't worry Moll, we are all together and I will look after you.'

Drake was met at the door by a very serious little daschund carrying a small wand and wearing a long black cloak. He led them down to the front of the church where seats were reserved for the whole family. They all sat in the pew and then finally Drake sat on the end. Tebor was very excited by all the little lights on the enormous Christmas tree at the front of the church.

'How do they do that Paddy?'

'It beats me Tebor. Must have to lower the lights down from the ceiling.'

'Perhaps the angels put the lights on,' said Murphy all knowingly.

'Don't be silly Murphy, angels don't do that sort of thing.'

The little group of puppies were all together and very excited and Pru turned to them and put her paw up to her lips, 'Sssh,' she whispered. 'Remember what we said, absolute silence, then there will be treats on the way home.' Everyone was quiet and the service began.

The organ started playing an old familiar carol and there were candles in all the windows and lanterns hanging throughout the building. The choir walked on down through the middle of the cathedral, they were all in red and white. A mixture of young puppies at the front and then more older singers following behind and finally the grand figure of Bishop

Rodney himself all dressed in purple with a big purple hat on his head and walking with a bishop's stick.

Paddy sat next to Mollie and she continued to stare right up into the ceiling. She looked very worried about something and Paddy kept turning to her and saying, 'Don't worry Moll it will be all right,' but she wasn't happy.

Paddy also could hear some creaking noises with his special hearing. 'What is going on Mollie?' he asked.

'I am not sure Paddy.'

The service started and Bishop Rodney stood quite close to them in the middle of the church.

Right up above him high in the church was a great big glass light fitting. The service started off with everyone standing up singing carols and then there were readings and eventually it came to the point where Bishop Rodney was going to talk to them all. He started off telling them the Christmas Story the way they had heard it told before by the Reverend Chumley in their own little church. Mollie was peering up into the darkness above him, and she could see that the light fitting was starting to swing.

Paddy could hear lots of creaking noises and Moll turned to Paddy and said, 'The light above him is going to fall down.'

Paddy rushed forward and pushed past his father who tried to grab him as he went by. Pru looked terribly frightened as Paddy rushed forward and pushed Bishop Rodney to one side.

Bishop Rodney let out a gasp and fell to the floor and at that minute the big light fitting fell and crashed down beside him. Fortunately it missed him and just caught the end of his purple gown. There was a big sigh from the congregation as they all rushed forward to see if Bishop Rodney was all right.

He stood up and pulled his gown from under the light fitting and shook himself. Then he turned to everyone in the congregation and said, 'It's all right, I'm safe. Thanks to this young puppy here who rushed out and pushed me to one side.

My life has been saved tonight.' He turned to Paddy and said, 'What is your name?'

'My name is Paddy.'

'Thank you Paddy. You saved my life tonight.' Everyone in the church stood up and clapped their paws loudly. Pru and Drake came out and very proudly led Paddy back into the seat where Moll was waiting for him.

'Well spotted Moll,' said Paddy. 'I could hear something was happening up there.'

Bishop Rodney told everyone that they must continue the service as normal and they sang some more carols and everyone started to go home. As the service was all over Drake and Pru led the way back across the lawn in front of the cathedral to where Bishop Rodney lived, where they had all been invited to go back for hot drinks and snacks. While they were there Bishop Rodney came across and thanked Paddy again for what he did in the church tonight.

Paddy said, 'You must also thank my sister, she is the one who saw something was wrong.'

Bishop Rodney said, 'I thank her too and I thank every one of your family and thank you Drake and Pru for the quick action of your young puppies who saved my life tonight.'

All the other puppies were very excited. Murphy was pulling away at Pru's arm. 'What is it Murphy, what is it?'

'Mummy can I be a Bishop when I grow up please?' They all laughed and said, 'Perhaps one day, if you're very good.'

After they had had tea and cakes at Bishop Rodney's, they said their goodbyes and they set off for home. As soon as they were settled in "the truck" Pru said, 'Well you were all marvellous tonight, and I promised you a treat, well you're going to get two.' She reached down and got some chocolates and passed these around.

'Thanks Mum,' said Murphy, 'but what is the other treat?'

'Well tomorrow we are going to make the Christmas cake

and I want you all to help. We will all have to stir the cake and you can each make a wish. But what we will do tomorrow will be slightly different. When you have made your wish I am going to get you all to draw on a piece of paper what you would like for Christmas. Then we will go to the big fireplace in the hall and one by one we will throw each piece of paper onto the fire so that your wish will go up the chimney to Father Christmas and then he will know what you want. I can't promise he will be able to provide everything, but we will see what we can do.'

The puppies were eating away at their chocolates and very excited about what they should wish for. They hadn't realised that already they were up on the mountain road and that they were looking back at the lights of Foldingham well behind them in the distance. They could see the cathedral with its tall spire still lit up in the darkness. One by one in the back seat they fell asleep while whispering to each other what they would like to have for Christmas.

Mollie and Paddy were still awake however and Mollie was looking very worried.

'Do you think Christmas will ever come Paddy? I can't think what to wish for.'

'There, there Mollie, close your eyes and have a rest now,' said Paddy and put his paw around her. Then they both closed their eyes and drifted off to sleep. Drake drove down the other side of the mountain and into Drakeshead down to the little village. The lights were on at the pub and music could be heard as they drove past the village green and up the drive to The Hall. There was already a Christmas tree with twinkling lights at either side of the doorway and there was a large holly wreath on the door. As they pulled up the puppies woke up and one by one they were stretching and making suggestions for what they would like to put on their wish list for Santa Claus. Stubbings was waiting at the door and had drinks for them all before they headed off to bed.

Drake could not believe what had happened at the cathedral that night and he said to all the puppies, 'We should be very grateful for what Paddy did tonight and it will be remembered by the people of Foldingham for years to come. Well done Paddy and well done to all of you for being so good at the cathedral tonight.' They all went off to bed very proud.

Drake turned to Pru and said, 'I can't believe what happened tonight. I tried to stop Paddy from running out because I thought he was being naughty, but all along he was saving Bishop Rodney. He and Mollie really are quite special aren't they?'

Pru smiled to herself and said, 'They certainly are Drake.' She only wished she could tell him how special they really were.

CHAPTER EIGHT

STIR UP SUNDAY

The next day the puppies were up very early. They were very excited because they knew that today was the day they were going to make the Christmas cake and they could make their wishes for the presents they wanted.

Stubbings had been busy in the kitchen and had made all the preparations for the cake. Pru told them all they must be ready in the late afternoon and then they would set to and put the finishing touches to the cake. When the time came all seven of them came into the kitchen and they all had on their little aprons, each one of them in the colour of the chair they normally sat in. They stood around the kitchen table and there was a great big bowl in the middle which was full of Christmas cake mix.

Pru was dressed up in her apron and was wearing her half-moon glasses on the end of her nose and was looking very serious. She watched as they all came in and gathered around the table. Murphy thought no one was watching and reached forward with his paw to grab some of the mixture to eat.

Pru just caught sight of him out of the corner of her eye and shouted out very loudly, 'Don't even think of it Murphy,' at which point he pulled back his paw very quickly and looked very innocent, but everyone knew that meant he was guilty. Drake came in to join them as well and Stubbings was there to help out. Pru got a very big wooden spoon and started stirring the cake.

'Now puppies, I want you to come along one by one and stir the cake. When you stir the cake mixture you have to make a wish.'

One by one they all came along and had their turn at stirring the cake. Finally little Murphy coming along, grabbing the spoon and stirring away at the cake, shouting out very loudly, 'I want to be a Bishop when I grow up.'

They all laughed and Pru shouted, 'Murphy you're not meant to tell anybody what your wish is.'

After they had all finished Drake came and he was the last person to stir the cake. Then they all went into the lounge where there was a big fire roaring away. The fire had the guard around it and they were all warned to keep well away from the fire. Pru then told them that as she had promised they were all given a little piece of paper each and a pencil and they were to draw on this what they wished for a present for Christmas. No one was to let anyone else know what they were drawing as it was all to be a big secret.

Mollie looked around the room and she could see exactly what everyone was drawing, but she didn't say anything to anyone, as she knew what she wanted. If ever asked, she wanted a white coat and a doctor's outfit and she drew this on her piece of paper. The others all drew what they wanted and Pru told them to fold up their pieces of paper so no one else could see. They all gathered around the fireplace and Pru said, 'One by one what we have got to do now is throw our little picture onto the fire and the smoke will go up the chimney so that Santa Claus will know what you want for Christmas.'

One by one they took a turn to throw their little drawing onto the fire and watched it burn away while the smoke went up the chimney. When that was all done it was time to start to decorate the Christmas tree. All the lights and coloured baubles and tinsel were all there in boxes, and Drake climbed up the ladder and put them on as they were passed to him, each puppy in turn bringing him a new item to put on the tree. There was a big tree in the lounge and then a very big tree in the dining room and in the hallway next to Pru's big old pink chair there was a wintry scene with lots of little lights on it all twinkling in the darkness showing a scene of Christmas past. Christmas was taking shape at The Hall. The puppies had stirred the cake, which was now in the oven cooking, they had made their wishes and the decorations were up. They were very excited and could hardly wait for Christmas.

CHAPTER NINE

THE NIGHT BEFORE CHRISTMAS

Christmas was a time that Pru had always loved at The Hall. Drake always made a point of being home from sea and of course this time he was home with her and the puppies. Pru always made a point of being well prepared for Christmas and she wanted the puppies to grow up with all the old traditions that The Hall carried with it.

Christmas Day was a big day at The Hall. They would all go to church on Christmas morning and then there would be the big Christmas lunch with them all around the table in the dining room. The night before Christmas was the time when the last things were done to the house. Big branches of holly were brought into The Hall together with lots of trailing ivy. There were fresh flowers put in every room, and the fires were all laid ready for the next morning. There were still a few little final touches that Pru liked done to the Christmas trees, and Drake did these after the puppies had gone off to bed, putting some little presents on the trees for the puppies for the following morning. The puppies were extremely excited and did not think they would be able to sleep at all. Pru and Drake were keen they should get a good night's sleep and got them off to bed quite early. They did the finishing touches and sat and had a final drink in front of the fire with all the lights on the trees glistening ready for Christmas Day.

Drake yawned and said, 'I don't know about you Pru, but I am ready for bed.'

Pru said, 'You go on up Drake as I have a few things left to do and I will come and join you later.'

He gave her a peck on the cheek and he went off to bed

leaving her alone by the fire. All the little lights in the hallway were on and she went out and sat in her old chair in the hallway and thought about Christmas and about all the preparations she had made and how everything was ready. She could see into the lounge and up the stairs and the magical world that had been created around the house. She knew she had a few more little jobs to do to get everything ready for the puppies before morning, but she yawned and her eyes felt heavy and before she knew it she was drifting off to sleep and her half-moon glasses were slipping off the end of her nose.

She awoke with a jolt as her chair was rising in the darkness, up through the hallway passed the twinkling lights halfway up the stairs and out into the night through the French windows. Where was the chair taking her on this cold winter's night? The air was cold as she breathed in through her nostrils and she shivered a little. The night sky was full of millions of stars and she looked around at them. Below her the ground was covered in thick snow. She did not remember it snowing recently.

She went up past the cockerel on the church clock who was frozen to the spot with icicles hanging off him. She gave him her usual little flick with her paw but he did not spin round. She looked at the church clock and it was showing eleven o'clock at night.

She noticed what looked like a much older chair than hers, like a rocking chair, coming towards her in the night sky. As it got closer she noticed a frail old Labrador with a white shawl around her head, and she did not recognise her for a moment. As the chair came nearer she knew it was Moll Doggins. She had seen pictures of her in the hallway and of all her ancestors who had lived at The Hall before her.

Pru said nothing but Moll turned to her and said, 'Follow me Pru, I am going to take you back to show you some of the secrets of how life used to be at The Hall at Christmas time many years ago.'

Both chairs spun around very rapidly and Pru felt a bit dizzy. The chair slowed down and gradually Pru found herself going back through The Hall's landing window and the chair came down in the hallway and it was quickly followed by Moll Doggins in her rocking chair. The two of them sat side by side but it wasn't The Hall she had just left instead it was The Hall of a hundred years before and even the furniture was different. There was also an elegant Dalmatian footman wearing tails who approached them with drinks on a silver tray. They both got off their chairs and Pru followed Moll around the house.

'You see Pru it is Christmas Eve and the house is ready.'

The one thing Pru noticed that was just the same was the grandfather clock in the hallway and it was the same one they had to this day.

Moll pointed out, 'There we are, at the stroke of midnight Santa Claus will come down the big chimney and bring all the presents.'

'But I didn't think he existed,' said Pru.

'He exists all right,' said Moll, 'and tonight you will meet him. Come with me.' They went into the old drawing room and took their seats.

'There are traditions Pru that you must take back with you. The puppies are all prepared and have sent their wishes off and we must make sure they have what they want.'

'I have lots of presents wrapped up for them,' said Pru, 'and Santa Claus will be bringing lots more.'

There was a great big tree in the drawing room covered in little tiny twinkling candles. The house was bathed in light from oil lamps and trays of food were brought in by the Dalmatians. There were lovely little sandwiches that Pru ate and lots of cakes with strawberry jam in them, which surprised Pru, but she wasn't going to spoil things and ask any questions tonight about the Squirmits. Moll Doggins led her over to the big piano and on top of this was a big white snowman.

'Every year Pru, we put presents in the snowman and at lunch time on Christmas Day I lift the lid off and hand out presents to people. I want you to take this snowman back with presents for the puppies.'

Pru wondered how she would get it back because it was very large.

'Don't worry Pru there will be no problems.' The other Dalmatians carried the snowman to Pru's chair and it was left there until she was ready to go. At that point the big hall clock struck twelve, one, two and as it was striking Moll led Pru back into the drawing room. They sat beside the little wine table which had some mince pies on it and a glass of sherry waiting for Santa Claus.

At the twelfth stroke there was a big thud down the chimney as Santa Claus, a big rosy faced St. Bernard, came down the chimney all dressed in red clothes with a big white beard. He was carrying a big sack. He brushed off the snow from his clothes and came out and greeted Moll Doggins.

'Santa Claus, I would like you to meet Pru.'

They shook hands and Pru said how thrilled she was to meet him at last. They sat and he had his sherry and his mince pies, and he emptied out his sack of presents onto the carpet in front of the fireplace and Pru put them under the tree ready for the following day. Before they knew it he was gone on his travels. He had many more visits to make before the morning.

'Well Pru, now you have met him, you know he exists,' said Moll. 'I want you now to go back and take the snowman with you, and have a wonderful Christmas tomorrow. Everything should be as it should be for the puppies. Everything has always been the same in The Hall and it will always be that way.'

'That is the way it will be,' said Pru as she headed back to the hallway and got onto her chair. Before she knew it the chair was rising from the hallway and was going out through the old

French windows. The chair rose up into the sky and spun rapidly around. The icy cold air was making her nostrils sore. In next to no time the chair was slowing down again and was coming back down past the church and then through the French windows. She landed in the hallway. The old clock was striking its twelfth strike again as she woke up and she rubbed her eyes. Had she imagined the whole thing? Had she really met Santa Claus? Probably she had dreamt it all because she had only been asleep for a very short time. But wait, what was this on the chair next to her? A big white snowman. Where had this come from? She could not have dreamt this. She picked the snowman up and put it in the hallway on the big table ready for the following day. Then she put out the lights and went to bed.

CHAPTER TEN

CHRISTMAS DAY

Christmas morning came, and Pru and Drake were awoken by the noise of the puppies chattering to each other and running around at the top of the stairs. They had been playing since six o'clock in the morning.

One by one they all came into the bedroom in their dressing gowns, that is apart from Murphy who was missing. Drake and Pru sat up in bed and looked around for Murphy. They put on their dressing gowns and together with the puppies tiptoed to the top of the stairs to find Murphy creeping down towards the presents.

'Don't even think of it Murphy,' shouted Pru from the top of the stairs, at which point everyone peered over the banisters and broke into laughter.

Murphy crept back upstairs looking very sorry for himself. 'I was only going to get a drink Mum I'm sorry,' said Murphy.

'A likely story I am sure Murphy. Anyway now we're all awake I am sure Stubbings will be getting breakfast ready for us, so we may as well go down and get started.'

They all gathered in the kitchen where sure enough breakfast was waiting. Stubbings was wearing her Christmas apron and had some tinsel in a little crown on her head. She had been up from a very early hour making sure everything was ready and she was preparing the big lunch for later on that day.

Breakfast was very noisy and all the puppies seemed to be eating at twice the normal speed in an attempt to get finished and open their presents. Paddy had his normal bowl of 'Ready Bark' with milk poured over it and the others had various breakfast cereals. Murphy was too excited to eat anything at all.

Mollie looked quite worried and anxious and turning to Paddy she said, 'There won't be any unpleasant presents will there Paddy?'

'No Moll,' said Paddy breaking off from a big spoonful of 'Ready Bark'. 'They will all be nice things today and I expect we'll all get what we asked for just you wait and see…'

When breakfast was over they were keen to get to the drawing room and open their presents. They were heading out of the room when Drake turned to them and said, 'Just a minute, before we leave the table who must we thank for all her hard work?'

The puppies looked at each other puzzled and one said, 'We must thank Mum.'

'Yes,' said Drake, 'you should thank Mum, but first we should all thank Stubbings who has been up from a very early hour getting our breakfast ready and preparing lunch. What do you say puppies?'

They all stood in line and turned to Stubbings and shouted, 'Thank you Stubbings and a Happy Christmas.'

Stubbings beamed a broad smile and wiped a tear from her eye with her apron. 'There there, you puppies are all worth it, go on with you now and open your presents.'

So they all rushed out of the dining room with their tails wagging, so that their little dressing gowns were flying from side to side as they went. They entered the drawing room to see the wonderful sight of dozens of presents piled around the tree. The tree reached up to the ceiling and was ablaze with coloured lights. The fire was roaring and either side of the fireplace were stockings full of presents and another big sack full of presents in the middle of the room.

'It looks like we have some very lucky puppies today Mum,' said Drake to Pru as he opened up the big sack. 'Now puppies these are all presents from Santa Claus who brought them down the chimney last night for you and left them here.' One by one he handed out several presents to each puppy all in colourful paper with labels with their names on.

Great excitement followed with paper flying in all directions as the puppies opened up their presents. Then their stockings were handed out to them and each one contained little piles of toys, sweets, clothes and goodies. Murphy meanwhile, having finished opening his presents, was gathering together all the wrapping paper and had piled it all together in a big ball and was just about to throw it onto the fire when Pru caught sight of him and barked across the room, 'Don't even think of it Murphy, not even on Christmas Day.'

Murphy dropped the bundles of paper and slipped back quietly to the others. Mollie was looking very sad, but then she always did look sad.

Paddy came over to her and said, 'What's the matter Moll? You've had some lovely presents.'

'Yes I know Paddy, but I was able to see inside the wrappings of all the presents and even before I opened them I knew I hadn't got the present I asked for on Stir Up Sunday.'

'Never mind Moll, the day's not over yet, and I didn't get what I asked for either. Let's not spoil it for the others,' he said and so they cheered each other up and went back to their presents.

'Well,' said Drake, 'it's time you puppies were getting ready for church. I want you all dressed and down in a line in the hall by quarter to eleven so that we won't be late.'

They all rushed upstairs and got themselves dressed up in their best little suits and dresses, and were ready waiting in the hallway on time. Drake and Pru came down the grand staircase looking magnificent walking arm in arm. Drake was in his admiral's outfit, and Pru was very splendid in her best clothes and finest jewellery. 'One has to make an effort for the village,' she would say.

Stubbings opened the front door for them and they left,

Drake and Pru leading the way, and the puppies following behind. Drake knew Pru liked to arrive spot on time once everyone was settled in the church, and sure enough that's how it was. The church was full and the service was about to begin when the family made their grand entrance and made their way to the family pew at the front of the church. The puppies filed into the pew, and then finally Pru followed by Drake who closed the little wooden door to the side of the pew. Just in front of where Pru was sitting was a fireplace with a fire burning to keep her and the family warm during the service.

The service began with a carol and they all rose and sang loudly. Pru looked around the church and looked at the choir which was made up of young puppies, and thought how well they had all 'scrubbed up' for the day, and they all seemed to be singing perfectly in tune today and everyone in the congregation seemed very happy. The service progressed and the Reverend Chumley came around to his sermon. They all sat very patiently and listened to him, but after a while the puppies were soon getting restless and wanting to move around, and by now even Pru thought Reverend Chumley was overdoing it a bit for Christmas Day. Eventually she leaned forward and reached the poker and gave the fire in front of her a rather noisy poking. Little fits of laughter broke out around the church, and The Reverend Chumley went a bit red in the face and soon drew his sermon to a close. The service then ended with another carol. The whole congregation waited while Drake, Pru and the puppies left, Pru giving a little nod to various acquaintances on left and right as she walked down the aisle. Chumley wished them a happy Christmas as they left the church, and said 'good-bye' to them, and the little band made its way back up to the The Hall for lunch.

Once back home the puppies rushed to look at their presents again and the drawing room was full of noise. All the puppies had realised that they hadn't got the present they had asked for on Stir Up Sunday, but Paddy tried to re-assure them all that Mum had said there were more presents to come.

Meanwhile in the dining room everything was ready for Christmas dinner. Pru and Drake stood by the marble fireplace sipping sherry.

'Happy Christmas Pru my dear,' Drake said giving Pru a little kiss.

'And to you too Drake, a very Happy Christmas.'

Drake took a small gift-wrapped box from his jacket pocket and gave it to Pru. She opened it up to find a diamond necklace.

'It's lovely Drake,' said Pru and Drake put it around her neck. She looked at herself in the mirror over the fireplace 'that's gorgeous, absolutely gorgeous,' and gave Drake another little kiss. 'I've got a present under the tree here for you Drake,' she said and pulled out a large gift-wrapped parcel. Drake was puzzled what could it be.

'Well go on, open it up,' said Pru impatiently.

He ripped open the paper to find inside a painting of himself wearing his full admiral's outfit. 'When did you get that done Pru?'

'Oh I had it done from some photos we took when we met you back from your last trip. That's your ship in the background, and there is the sea in the distance.'

'It's wonderful my love, I look very proud in the picture.'

'And so you should be Drake,' she said, and he gave her a little kiss. So it was time for lunch. Drake called Stubbings and they sounded the gong. The puppies made their way into the dining room chattering away to each other. First Murphy rushed along stealing sweets from the side tables on the way, well it was Christmas Day and perhaps for once he just might get away with it. Bramley, Tebor and Bentley were next huddled together deep in conversation about their Christmas presents. Then Toffee came in dancing and doing a pirouette at one end of the dining table, then dancing around the table until coming to a stop at her place. Last of course were Paddy and Mollie and they lingered in the hallway after Mollie had noticed the large white snowman on the hall table.

'I don't remember seeing that before Paddy.'

'I noticed it this morning on the way to church,' replied Paddy. 'What's in it Mollie?'

'I can't quite see, but it looks like it's full of presents but I can only see parts of things. It's not clear, but there is lots of wrapping paper.'

'I wonder when we'll know?'

'Well I can't wait Paddy. Will we ever know what's inside the snowman?'

'Sure Moll, we'll have to be patient though until after lunch. Let's not mention it to the others. They probably wouldn't understand anyway. Keep it a secret between us two.'

So they joined the others for lunch, and Drake and Pru sat down one at each end of the dining table. The table was groaning with the weight of food. Course after course came in from the kitchen, and eventually they came to the arrival of the Christmas pudding, which was alight with a flickering flame and a sprig of holly on top and all the puppies went 'oooh' as this was cut up and passed around. They all emptied their bowls and licked their spoons clean of their very last bits of Christmas pudding and cream.

The meal over, Pru left the table and asked Drake if he would give her a hand, and then went into the hall, and between them they carried in the large snowman and put it on the table in front of Pru's place at the table.

'What's this all about Pru?' said Drake.

'Oh it's an old fashioned idea they used to do in The Hall many years ago. I believe it was in the days of Moll Doggins and I thought I would start it up again.' The puppies were all excited and sitting on the edge of their seats.

Paddy turned to Moll and whispered, 'See Moll, I said Mum would bring in the snowman after lunch, and now we'll know what's inside won't we?'

Pru stood up at her end of the table and taking a spoon she banged it on her table mat waiting for some silence. Once everyone was quiet she said, 'Now puppies listen to me. Inside the snowman there are presents for all of you, one present each. I know you haven't had the presents you asked for on Stir Up Sunday, but let's see what everyone is going to get from the snowman.'

Pru lifted up the large white head and they all saw a bright light shining from inside the snowman. There were little beams of stardust rising in the air as rays of the late afternoon sun poured in through the dining room window. It went very quiet around the table as the puppies stared at the sight. Their little mouths dropped open in wonderment and they all went 'oooh.'

Pru put her arm inside the snowman and went deeper and deeper as if feeling around for something. She then pulled out her arm with a present in her paw. The present was wrapped in sparkling paper and on the label it said to Nicole (Toffee) with all our love. She passed the present to Toffee who ripped open the wrapping paper to find a pair of dancing shoes.

'Just what I wanted and asked for.' She slipped them on and they were just the right size. She got up and danced around and around the table, doing dances she didn't even know she could do. She danced around a few times then she came to Pru and said, 'Thank you, thank you Mummy,' and then danced off into the distance again.

Next Pru's arm went back into the snowman and pulled out a present for Bramley. Bramley remained very serious and stayed that way even when he opened his present and revealed a policeman's helmet and a whistle. Pru thought for one moment she detected a slight smile on his face, but he was soon his usual self again.

'Is that what you wanted Bramley?' she said as he now had the hat on and was plodding back and forth in the dining room, stopping imaginary traffic with his whistle and holding his right paw up in a series of commands.

'Exactly,' he said, 'exactly,' and he continued with his imaginary duties.

Drake was sitting at the other end of the table with a smile on his face looking proudly at Pru and marvelling at how clever she was to have done this. Next out of the snowman came a very long present. It seemed bigger than the other two presents and seemed to be taller than the snowman. Pru lifted it out and passed it to Bentley. On the label it said 'To Bentley, my little gardener with love.'

Bentley opened up the paper and there inside was a spade a fork and trowel and packets of seeds with brightly coloured flowers on the covers. There was also a book on how to grow flowers. 'Oh thank you, thank you, thank you,' said Bentley. 'How did you know Mum that is what I wanted?'

Pru blushed a little. 'I think I know what you puppies would like. You don't keep it a secret do you?' There were still four anxious faces around the dining table.

'What's left inside Moll can you see?' asked Paddy quietly.

'It's not clear Paddy, it's just a jumble of things and a bright light inside.'

Next Pru lifted out another parcel wrapped in blue sparkling paper. She turned to Murphy and said, 'You know my little chappie, I have not told you off as often as usual today, but I have noticed you have been eating all the mince pies and you'll be sick if you carry on like that. Before I give you your present from the snowman, your Dad and I have one little gift for you. You know we're both hoarse with shouting at you when you're into mischief, so here's a T shirt for you to wear.'

Pru held up a T shirt and let it fall down revealing Murphy's face on the shirt and on the back it said 'Don't even think about it Murphy.'

Paddy, Mollie and Murphy were all laughing away at this. Murphy slipped it on over his shirt.

Drake came around to him and said, 'There you are my boy, when you see temptation, just look at the shirt and remember, *don't even think about it* my boy.'

Pru then passed him his present from the snowman. The bright light was still shining out from the snowman and twinkling in the light from the setting sun outside. The dining room was now bathed in soft glow coming from the candles on the table all around the room. Pru passed his present over to him. He sat looking very cheekily with his head on one side and he reached out and opened it to reveal bags and bags of sweets, but inside the sweets was another present wrapped again in sequined paper. He opened this slowly to find a prayer book. He opened up the prayer book and inside it inscribed on the front page it said: 'To Murphy, this prayer book was once the property of Moll Doggins of The Hall.'

He rushed over to his Mum and gave her a kiss, 'Thank you Mum. It's what I've always wanted my own prayer book. One day I will be a real vicar like the Reverend Chumley.'

Pru laughed and looked at Drake, 'What a funny little fellow he is, always into trouble but with such a serious side to him. Whatever will become of him?'

Just three puppies left now, and Pru turned to Tebor who wanted to get his present and get back to Bentley and Bramley, as the three of them were always huddled together discussing things. Pru reached into the snowman and pulled out Tebor's gift and passed it to him. It was a large present and it was hard to see how it had come out of the snowman. When he opened it up he found sets of screwdrivers and models to make in metal, with little screws with batteries and bulbs, and trays and trays of little parts.

Tebor couldn't get started quickly enough, and was starting to leave the table with his big box when he looked back with his big staring eyes, 'Thank you Mum just what I wanted.'

As he passed Drake, his father said, 'Aren't you a lucky fellow. I'll come and help you with building the models when we have finished because I am sure it will be very hard.'

So that just left Mollie and Paddy sitting side by side at the dining table. Mollie looked sad, but then Moll always looked sad.

'Only two of you to go now,' said Pru. 'I suppose you two know what you want to receive from the snowman. Let's hope there is something left inside for you shall we? It seems very empty but I'll dig down deep and see if there is anything left near the bottom,' said Pru putting her whole arm deep into the snowman. She pulled out her arm holding a sparkling packet with Mollie's name on it and passed it across. 'There my little Moll, don't think we would miss you out.'

Mollie opened up the parcel and inside was a doctor's white coat with a stethoscope and all the gadgets a doctor would use. Mollie leapt off her chair and put the white coat on and had the stethoscope around her neck and was listening to her heart lub dub, lub dub, lub dub.

'I can hear my heart beating!' she shouted. 'Thank you Mum, how did you know I wanted a doctor's kit?'

Pru put her paw to her lips, 'Sssh my little one, that's my secret, but one day I'll tell you. Well that only leaves you Paddy boy.'

Mollie had stayed waiting with him but was engrossed in listening to her heart, and then she decided she would inspect Paddy's ears.

He brushed her off with his paw, 'Not now Moll, it's my turn, you can look in my ears later.' Paddy had now moved up and was sitting next to Pru getting very excited and right up as close as he could to the snowman.

'I hope there is one left in there for you Paddy. Drake while I give Paddy his present, will you let Stubbings know we'll take tea in the drawing room in fifteen minutes please.'

Drake slipped out whilst Pru pulled out two very large presents. They were much taller than the snowman and seemed to go on and on and on for such a long time. She then passed them to Paddy, and then four more round presents came out of the snowman and then several more, all of which were so large that they could not have been inside the snowman, but neither Mollie nor Paddy asked any questions, and the others were not there to see.

Paddy put all the pieces in front of the big fire, and opened them one by one to find four wheels for a tractor and all the other parts.

'Lay them all on the floor,' said Pru, 'and stand back,' and as he did some blue smoke came down the chimney and covered the parts of the tractor. The wheels stood up and joined the axles, and the body of the toy tractor formed in front of them. The blue smoke swirled around and then whisked back up the chimney. Both Paddy and Mollie were amazed and stared at the sight in front of them. Even Pru was shocked, but she had learned through the years not to be surprised by anything.

'Mum a tractor, just what I wanted.'

'Well go on then sit on it if you like,' said Pru, and without any effort, the tractor drove up and down the dining room.

Drake walked back in at that point, 'Stubbings will have tea ready for us very soon my love.' He saw Paddy on his tractor and said, 'Where did that come from?'

'It's Paddy's present from the snowman, it's a bit large and I needed some help putting it together, but all is done now.'

'It's wonderful Pru, did some of the village folk help you?'

'Well shall we say Drake, I had some help' said Pru.

'Well done my dear, I think the snowman was a great

success, and from what you say we have Moll Doggins to thank for the idea.'

'We certainly do,' said Pru, and I don't know how I'll ever thank her for her help and kindness.'

They all moved through to the drawing room and had tea, and everyone was so excited the time passed very quickly, and the rest of the day was soon over. All the puppies took their presents up to bed with them, apart from Paddy whose tractor was too large to get up the stairs. Drake yawned and said it was time he went upstairs. He kissed Pru who said she had a little tidying up to do and would soon follow. As she made her way into the dining room she passed Moll Doggins' painting in the hallway.

She turned to the picture and whispered, 'Thank you Moll Doggins, it all went very well today, especially thanks to you.'

Pru felt she sensed a smile back from the painting and a little wink in response, but the lighting was getting very dim now. She went into the dining room and started to blow out the candles one by one. The snowman was still sitting at her place at the table, and as she blew out the candles the head of the snowman turned to face her, but it was no longer the snowman's face she could see in the shadows of the candles, but that of Albos, the Goddog.

He smiled at her and said, 'Well done Pru, I will send you help to train Paddy and Mollie soon, do not worry. Now away to bed, and get some rest.'

She looked again and now could only see the snowman's face looking back at her. Was the light playing tricks? She blew out the last few candles and went to bed.

CHAPTER ELEVEN

THE NEW YEAR

Christmas had been an exciting time at The Hall, the puppies had had all the presents they had asked for and more besides. Each of them had played endlessly with their new toys. Toffee marvelled at dances she could do in her new shoes that she had never even dreamt of doing before. Bramley never stopped organising everyone in his new helmet, and Tebor constructed magnificent toy models with flashing lights and whirling motors – the little screws and nuts magically turning themselves into place. Moll was in her element diagnosing little ailments in all the others, and had made Stubbings undergo a full medical, much against her will, and of course Paddy had virtually worn out the carpet going back and forth on his tractor.

The days after Christmas had gone by very quickly, Pru had had Drake at home and the family had been together over the last few months, but she knew he was ready to go off to sea again on another adventure. The puppies were due to start school, and although it was only around the corner from The Hall, it was a big step in their lives. Pru was finding she needed more help in looking after them, and knew that Paddy and Mollie's special powers needed extra training, and hoped it wouldn't be too long before Albos sent her that help he had promised.

In the early days of the New Year the sky started to go very grey and the wind started to roar around the village. The little cockerel on the church spire swung around and around and settled to show that the cold wind was blowing from the east.

It started snowing lightly and soon the ground was white all over. The puppies wrapped up in their little duffle coats and

Wellingtons and rushed out to play in the drifting snow. They made a big snowman like the one with presents in that Mum made at Christmas. Then they ran around throwing snowballs at each other.

The snow got heavier and it became much colder, so that even the puppies no longer wanted to go out to play but to stay in the warmth of The Hall. The skies were growing much darker and it did not really become light at all during the day. The wind was blowing stronger and whistling around The Hall, and as the puppies sat looking through the drawing room window they could see flocks of very dark black birds casting shadows across the grey skies.

There was a large fire in the drawing room and Pru called the puppies away from the window, 'Come across away from there and sit on the sofa.'

She wrapped them in blankets to keep them warm. Pru and Drake stood in front of the puppies with their backs to the fire. 'We're in for a bad winter,' Drake told them all. 'I won't be able to go to sea until all this has passed, and you puppies won't be able to start school until it's all over. We've lots of food in the cellar so we won't starve, but there won't be many treats for some time.'

There was a large bang as a big piece of ice fell off the roof and landed in the garden and the puppies rushed to the window. The snow was coming down in large clusters, the trees were thrashing around in the winds and the sky remained black with menacing birds being tossed around in the grey skies. Mollie didn't like what she saw and was trembling.

Paddy as usual put a paw around her shoulder, 'Don't worry Moll, we'll be quite safe in The Hall and there is plenty to eat and drink.'

'I know Paddy, but I can't see any end to the storms. I can normally see through the clouds and know the sun will return again soon.'

All the puppies looked sad as they looked through the window. Murphy seized the opportunity and had his prayer book open and started to pray for everyone to be delivered from the storm. Toffee put on her dancing shoes and tripped off across the hall thinking she was a snow fairy. Bramley was acting his usual sensible self and was directing the remaining puppies in an orderly way back to the sofas and explaining where the emergency exits were in case of a crisis.

Drake called everyone to order again, 'I suggest we make the most of a bad job and settle down with our books and games by the fire.'

Stubbings came in with trays of hot cocoa and they all settled around the fireplace. Stubbings put up the shutters and closed the curtains. Drake threw a large log on to the fire and as the winds roared outside the flames rushed up the chimney causing a warm bright glow around the room.

'Are you all right in the kitchen Stubbings?' asked Drake.

'Yes, sir, but I fear the water will freeze soon, it's just like the winter of 1947 I remember it well, it was a nightmare, sir. In the villages all around puppies were found frozen in their beds, the churchyards were full of them. Have you ever read the gravestones, sir? They make sad reading all those young ones lost, like the old stories they used to tell in the olden days about the battle of the clouds. It won't be like that this time, sir, will it? Please say we'll be spared and all the little ones, please don't let it be like the battle of the clouds.'

'That's enough of talk like that Stubbings, not in front of the family. Now go back to your work you know we'll all be safe in The Old Hall. You keep nice and warm by the stove in the kitchen and thank you for the cocoa.'

The puppies were huddled together on the two sofas in their dressing gowns. Mollie was crying and Paddy had his arm around her. Murphy had his right paw raised and was holding a prayer book and blessing everyone.

Then he rushed over to Drake, 'Will that mean there will be lots of funerals at the churchyard Dad?' he asked with excitement.

'Settle down Murphy,' said Pru. 'It's only a storm, and we don't know do we, it may be over by morning.'

Toffee had returned from another dancing spree and they all sat drinking their cocoa on the sofas.

Drake and Pru took their seats on either side of the fireplace and they also settled down to drink their cocoa.

'What was Stubbings talking about – the story of the battle of the clouds Mum?' asked Paddy.

'Oh it's just an old nonsense story going back deep in time, you don't want to trouble your heads with that.'

The others all sat forwards on their sofa, except for Moll who wasn't sure, all pleading, 'Go on Mum let's have a story like the one you used to tell us about the days when Moll Doggins was here at The Hall, go on please tell us, tell us, tell us.'

'No you don't want to trouble your heads with that old nonsense,' said Drake.

'Please Dad we should hear these old stories,' said Paddy.

'Oh well, perhaps I should tell them,' said Pru. 'It's a very, very old story long before the days of Moll Doggins and long before The Hall was built and anyone lived in the village,' she said. 'It seems that in those days the skies overhead were clear blue apart from wispy white clouds which moved gently across the sky. The sun shone brightly and when it got too hot the white clouds blew softly on the earth cooling it down. The white clouds would gather and blow gently together and when rain was needed they would sprinkle warm showers on the earth so that the plants grew and the land was green. Everyone was happy and believed that the white clouds were the home of the Goddogs.'

'What's a Goddog?' asked Paddy.

'They say they are absolutely pure white Labradors that live in the white clouds and they look down on us and watch us to keep us safe,' said Pru.

By now all the puppies were on the edge of their seats, 'And do these Goddogs really exist?' asked Murphy.

'Well Murphy some believe they do and who are we to question them,' replied Drake.

'I'll continue,' said Pru not wanting to go too far down that line of discussion at the moment.

'Well,' said Paddy, 'what could ever go wrong when everyone was so happy with the Goddogs watching over them?'

'That's where the story continues,' said Pru. 'They say that long, long ago there was the battle of the clouds when the black clouds moved in over the skies and tried to destroy the white clouds. The black clouds made the earth grow dark and caused the land to be cold and they say these were the clouds where the Garudogs lived. These were big black beasts with the head of a dog with five eyes, but with the body of a bird with large black wings that flapped to cause the clouds to fly through the sky quickly. The story goes that these Garudogs took control of the skies and a battle raged for several years. The Garudogs raced across the skies making the land black and they fired silver arrows at the white clouds which rained down on the land destroying the crops and the earth. The land became cold and the ground froze.'

Mollie was looking very frightened by now, 'Is that why Stubbings thought this was the battle of the clouds again Mum?' she asked.

'Yes,' Pru said, 'but don't be afraid this will all pass and this is only a story.' She tried to re-assure her, 'So back to the story,' said Pru. 'Everyone thought that the Garudogs had won and the earth would stay in darkness for ever, but the Goddogs gathered together all the energy they had and the white clouds started to blow together. They blew so hard that they blew all the black clouds and the Garudogs out of the sky and they won the battle of the clouds. Once again the sun shone back on the earth and the land was warm again and the Goddogs drifted across the skies in the white clouds gently, gently blowing down on the land when it got too warm again. So you see puppies, although it's a sad story it has a happy ending in the same way that this storm will pass and we'll all be back to normal again.'

One of the puppies then said, 'Are these big blackbirds in the sky the Garudogs Mum?'

'No dear, they are just birds being blown around by the storm and you must not worry about them.' Pru thought to herself perhaps they were, but did not really want to let the others know this. 'You see puppies the story has a happy ending like all the ones I tell you. I don't want you to worry your little heads about the storm that is raging outside because probably by tomorrow it will be all over and then we can start getting you all ready for your first day at school. Now drink up your cocoa and all go off to bed and keep warm. There are extra blankets for all the beds and you'll all have your hot water bottles.'

One by one they came and kissed Pru and Drake goodnight and headed off to bed. When they had all gone up to bed Drake said, 'I don't know why you tell them these old stories Pru, putting strange ideas into their heads, at their age they will believe anything.'

'Well Stubbings brought up the old story of the battle of the clouds and they wouldn't be content until they knew it,' said Pru. 'Anyway they are growing up now and they can easily cope, apart from little Moll who always worries. It's a good job Paddy always keeps an eye on her, I expect she'll surprise us in years to come and become quite fearless.'

'We'll have to wait and see Pru dear, now I'm off to bed you won't be long after me will you?'

'I'll be with you as soon as I've checked everything is OK. I won't be long. You run along now and get some rest,' said Pru.

Pru got up and put the guard in front of the fire and watched the last embers of the fire glowing. How comforting she thought the flames were when it was so miserable outside. She turned out the lights and closed the drawing room door. The grandfather clock was ticking away in its re-assuring way and the light over Moll Doggins' picture lit up her face.

Pru stopped and looked at her, 'I wonder about these old stories Moll, the more I get to know the more I think they are probably true. I hope the storm will ease soon.'

She sat for a moment in her old chair in the hall, something she hadn't done for quite a while now. As she drifted off to sleep the old chair started to rise and the French windows were thrown open in the same way as before. She opened her eyes with a start because she didn't want to be taken out in the storm, but as she went out on the chair she didn't feel the cold and the biting east wind had gone.

The chair took her up and over the church and the cockerel was now swinging around on its spire and was showing that the wind had changed and was now coming from the west. Pru sat up and looked down and even in the darkness with the bright moonlight she could see everywhere was white with drifting snow across the lanes. The chair rose upwards and seemed to be moving out of the darkness and she found herself entering a very white cloud which seemed to drift across the night sky It was just floating by in the light of the moon.

The chair and Pru just entered into the cloud in a casual way. It was light on the white cloud and there were two small pure white Labrador puppies with white wings sitting on the cloud. They came over to Pru and sat on the arms of her chair, one on either side of her.

They looked at her and one said, 'The storm will be over tomorrow Pru, the battle of the clouds as always has been won by the Goddogs. Albos cannot come to you but he is safe, and wanted you to know that all will be well and that you can soon start training with Paddy and Mollie. Once they have started the school in their village their training can begin. When you awake in the morning the weather will be warmer again and the dark clouds will be gone and the snow will start to clear. Be sure to help anyone who is suffering from the effects of the storms Pru, we know you will anyway.'

Pru wasn't sure what this meant and then the two puppies left her chair and rejoined the cloud, leaving her back on her old faithful chair in the moonlight in the darkness. The chair slowly turned and started to descend to the ground. The wind was already much warmer and when she got nearer the village the cockerel was set with the wind gently blowing from the west. The chair slowed up and came in through the French windows and landed back in the hall in its usual spot.

Pru heard the clock strike midnight and she awoke rubbing her eyes. Had she been dreaming again or was it true? She walked halfway up the stairs and opened the French windows to find a warmer wind blowing and she could hear the sound of water trickling off the roof as the ice was thawing.

She ran upstairs to tell Drake that the bad weather was over, but he was lying on his back snoring loudly. There was no point in disturbing him, but Paddy and Mollie stood at the bedroom door.

'The storm is over isn't it Mum? As you said the Goddogs would win as always,' said Mollie.

'Yes dears, it's all over and it will be fine tomorrow, now off to bed with you both.' she said giving them both a hug and a kiss. 'You knew anyway didn't you?'

The next morning they were all up early as the sound of ice breaking off the roof and water dripping had woken them. There was excitement in the kitchen over breakfast at the thought of getting out again and the thought of soon starting school caused a lot of chattering over their cereals and even Stubbings looked relieved that things had improved.

She was standing at the sink looking out of the window when she turned to Pru, 'Madam there is a very sad looking little fellow at the gate,' she said pointing.

Pru got up from the table and came over to the window and at the bottom of the drive was a little Scottie in a long coat trailing in the wet slush and snow. He had an extra long scarf wrapped around his neck several times, but still reaching to the ground and it was soaking wet in the snow. He wore a cap on his head and crept up the drive with his head hung low looking exhausted.

Stubbings said, 'The little fellow looks worn out, madam, shall I go and offer him help?'

'Yes,' said Pru, 'I'll come with you,' and they headed to the front door.

Drake wasn't sure. 'You be careful you two, you don't know who comes to the door these days, keep the chain on don't just let him in.' When they opened the door the little Scottie crept up the steps.

'Don't be silly messing with chains Stubbings, what harm can he do to us he looks exhausted.'

Pru stepped out and offered him a hand to come up the steps. He really was on his last legs and soaking wet with his clothes sodden by the melted snow and the slush.

Pru said, 'Stubbings fetch some warm towels and a dressing gown, use one of the puppy's dressing gowns, he is only such a little fellow. What's your name young man?'

'I'm Jock, I've been lost for days walking in the snow, I don't know where I am and I can't remember where I've come from.'

'A likely story,' said Drake who came out of the hall.

'Drake that's enough of that talk,' said Pru. 'Mr Jock needs help. Come along in and come straight into the cloakroom. Now get out of those wet clothes and put on a dressing gown. Then have a warm shower and come and join us in the kitchen by the stove for some hot coffee and breakfast and then we can talk about the future.'

Stubbings led Jock into the cloakroom and gave him a towel and a dressing gown. She could see he was soaking wet and struggling to stay awake.

'Get yourself a quick warm shower and come on into the kitchen once you're done,' she told him and she left him there.

Jock struggled to throw off his wet clothes then wiped his head with the towel and stepped into the warm shower. He hadn't felt warm for days and all his muscles ached with pain. He was so tired and he soon stepped out of the shower, quickly towelled himself dry and put on the dressing gown. He pulled the collar up around his neck but he was still shivering and he made his way cross the hall to the kitchen. It was lovely and warm in the kitchen and the puppies all rushed around him offering him a chair next to the Aga which he gladly took.

Pru came over with a mug of warm coffee and some toast which Stubbings had prepared. Jock's eyes widened at he sight of the food. He couldn't remember when he last ate or drank. He ate all the pieces of toast rapidly and drank the coffee down and soon was feeling very sleepy again, but now at last feeling warm and full.

'You're not going to stay awake long are you Mr Jock,' said Pru. 'I think the best thing is to find you a bed and let you sleep until you're feeling better and then we can have a talk and find out all about you.'

'And where you've come from,' said Drake rather sternly.

'Let him rest now,' said Pru. 'Stubbings has made up a bed in one of the upper guest rooms near to her room. There is a fire going and you'll be nice and warm and can sleep as long as you need then we'll catch up with you later.'

'Thank you so much your ladyship,' said Jock. 'Your kindness will not go unrewarded and when I'm feeling stronger I will repay you. I may look small and frail but I am strong and willing to help wherever possible.'

'Don't worry about that now,' said Pru. 'Stubbings will take you up to your room.'

The puppies had all watched in amazement at the newcomer. None of them were sure what to make of him. Murphy really didn't hold much hope for him when he appeared on the doorstep and went for his prayer book. As usual Bentley, Bramley and Tebor were huddled in conference discussing the pros and cons of a stranger turning up at their house. With Bramley being insistent that one couldn't be too sure these days about accepting strangers into one's home. Toffee took full advantage of the situation and started dancing up and down the hallway in a fairy-like way, wafting an imaginary magic wand in the air. That left Mollie and Paddy. Mollie was concerned about the newcomer.

'I hope this doesn't mean trouble Paddy.'

'Don't worry Moll,' said Paddy with his re-assuring paw on her shoulder. 'If it's all OK with Mum then there will be no problem.'

'But Dad didn't seem pleased that we were helping strangers,' said Moll.

'You know what Dad's like,' said Paddy. 'He has been away at sea for so long and he's met some strange types on his travels. So you see if Mum's happy then we should go along with her. I sense that Mum knows more about Mr Jock than we think.'

Mollie didn't know what Paddy was talking about but she felt re-assured and they joined the others in the hallway as they watched Stubbings lead the little visitor upstairs wearing one of their old dressing gowns.

The sun shone all that day and there were no more dark clouds in the sky and the large blackbirds had gone, and now the normal songbirds' voices filled the air. By the afternoon all the snow had gone and Pru walked around the garden with Drake in the warm afternoon sunlight. They toured the flowerbeds and now the snow was gone, the early purple and yellow crocuses were coming through and little clumps of snowdrops.

'It's marvellous to see spring on its way, the long dark days were so miserable,' said Pru. They held paws as they walked together and the birds sang beautifully as if welcoming the sunlight back. There sitting in a small tree at the end of the garden was their old friend Percy, The Hall pigeon, who had been around as long as they could remember. He sang his usual song and ruffled up his feathers as they passed.

'He's like an old friend,' said Drake, 'you gave him that name didn't you Pru?'

'You know I really can't remember,' said Pru. 'I must ask Stubbings, she may remember where it came from.'

The sun was now low in the sky and there was an evening chill in the air as they headed back into the conservatory.

'I hope you don't mind us taking care of the stranger Drake.'

'No Pru you are always so kind and considerate and thinking of others. I just wanted to make sure you were all safe. I will need to be going to sea again soon now that the weather has improved, and the puppies must start at school. We need to get some help for you and Stubbings and if the little fellow really is lost and has no memory he may want to stay here for a while and help out.'

Pru turned to Drake, 'We'll see if he has woken up yet shall we.'

They went into the kitchen to find Stubbings, 'Any sign of the little stranger waking Stubbings?'

'I've just been up to his room, sir, he's still fast asleep. I would say he'll sleep the clock around twice over at least.'

They laughed at the thought and said they would talk to him tomorrow. They all settled in and had their evening meal around the kitchen table. All the puppies were anxious to know if they could go up and see Mr Jock.

'Puppies, he is very tired and needs to get his sleep. Let him rest and we'll all talk to him in the morning.'

So they ate and chattered and got themselves ready for bed. They came into the kitchen one by one and said good night to Pru and Drake, each giving them a kiss. Stubbings put some food and drink on a tray to leave beside Jock's bed if he should wake in the night. They all then made their way to bed for a good night's sleep, thankful that the storms had gone and life at The Hall was back to normal. As Pru lay in bed she thought how nice it was to be back to normal. That's the way she liked life to be at The Hall and that's the way it always would be, but she just wondered would the arrival of the newcomer change anything. Then she drifted off to sleep.

CHAPTER TWELVE

THE PUPPIES START AT SCHOOL

The time had come for the puppies to start school. The bad winter had closed the school but now it was open again and all was planned for them to start. The boys all had their wine coloured blazers and shorts with wine and silver striped ties. The girls had similar blazers but with grey skirts rather than grey shorts. There were seven lunch boxes made up by Stubbings each one the colour of their old chairs they used to sit on.

They all lined up in the hallway ready for inspection. Drake and Pru checked each one, straightening their ties and picking the odd hair off their collars.

'Well you all look splendid,' said Drake, 'and I'm sure your mother agrees.'

Pru was nodding with approval. In the background Stubbings was beaming with pride at her little band of puppies all dressed up for school.

The village school was only around the corner past the church and the puppies knew it well having passed it regularly on their morning walks. Today would be different though as they only knew it from the outside. Today they would spend their first day there away from The Hall and their family. They were all excited but of course Mollie was a bit wary about what lay ahead, but she would have Paddy close by her at all times, so she felt safe.

So the little band set off being led by Pru and Drake, the puppies forming their usual groups of Paddy and Mollie, Bentley, Bramley and Tebor with Murphy at the rear and Toffee skipping between them always dancing as usual. Pru had to keep an eye on Murphy. They hadn't got very far when she noticed his shoelaces had become undone and he was tripping up. She had to stop the group and go back and sort him out, as he was in danger of falling over and hurting himself.

'Come along Murphy, you're always into mischief my little fellow.' Once sorted out they all headed on their way again. The school was small and had two teachers. The headmistress was a middle-aged retriever who wore glasses and her hair was spun up in a tight bun on her head. Her name was Miss Primbling or Primbo as she was to be nicknamed by the puppies. Miss Primbling was waiting outside the school to greet the new arrivals, seven new entrants on one day. She couldn't remember a time when there were so many new pupils.

She greeted Drake and Pru with great deference and told them how she would look after the family, and took them in and showed them their places in the classroom. There were only a few other pupils. Some of these the puppies knew from church or seeing them around the village, one or two however were new faces. They all settled in and had their first lessons.

Paddy sat next to Mollie so he could keep an eye on her. He noticed she was looking around the classroom at the other puppies and looked very wary, but all went well on the first day. They didn't go home for lunch, but had special sandwiches and treats which Stubbings had put in their boxes.

Mollie ate hers very quickly and soon turned to Paddy's box to see if there were any leftovers. How did she eat so fast he always thought as he shared his last biscuit with her. They played in the afternoon and the first day was soon coming to a close.

Pru was waiting for them at the classroom door and Miss Primbling presented them to her saying how well the first day had gone. Pru had a little biscuit treat for each of them as they walked home to The Hall all full of stories to tell. She noticed Murphy had entered into the spirit of the day, his shirt tail was hanging out and he had obviously fallen and scuffed his knees and of course both laces were still undone. She would have to have a little word with him later. Mollie and Paddy stayed close to Pru and explained the day's proceedings.

The three boys were as usual deep in conversation and Toffee kept dancing in her normal way. Stubbings was waiting on the steps back home and Jock was with her having fully recovered now after sleeping for forty-eight hours. Pru and Drake had quizzed him about where he had come from, but he had no memory other than walking for days in the cold and the snow.

He did however remember his only companion who kept talking to him as he walked along which was a black and white cat whom he remembered was called Tache, a French cat who was called that because of a black mark on the left side of his face and that Tache was French for mark or spot, and that was all he could remember. He didn't know what became of the cat or any other information. Drake had warmed to the little fellow, but thought he must be delirious and still rambling on about a black and white French cat.

Anyway he agreed to let Jock stay as he offered to help around the house and garden and look after the puppies. So there on the doorstep were Stubbings and Jock waiting to catch up on the day's events. Stubbings led them straight into the kitchen where she had freshly made lemonade, cakes and biscuits waiting as a welcoming home party for them after their first day. She wiped her paws and smoothed down her apron.

'You won't get this treatment every day puppies as today is special and Mr Jock and I want to hear all about your first day.'

After that it was non stop chatter in the kitchen as they all seemed to talk at once, all giving their own version of the same first day at school as viewed from another pair of tiny eyes. Drake joined Pru and they stood admiringly at the kitchen door listening to the happy stories being related in the kitchen by a group of puppies who sounded like they had been attending school all their lives rather than one day only.

Pru and Drake sat for a while in the drawing room and chatted, and Drake let it be known that he had decided it was time he was going back to sea again. Pru knew he was due to leave again and felt happier knowing that she and Stubbings had another pair of hands around to help look after the puppies and even Drake admitted that Jock made Pru a useful addition to the household, although he would have preferred to have had a bit more knowledge of his background.

That evening after dinner Drake informed the puppies that next weekend he was heading off to sea again for a while. The puppies all went quiet. They had had Dad at home several months and could not imagine life at home with him away again.

'It won't be for long this time puppies,' said Drake, 'and we'll all go to Foldingham at the weekend to see the boat and you can wave me off. Mr Jock is going to stay on and help your mother and Stubbings around the house and help look after you, so I want you all to promise that you'll be good and obedient and work hard at school, and that extends particularly to you Murphy. I don't even want you to think about being naughty,' he said waving his paw in Murphy's direction.

Where was Murphy? He was under the table finishing off a box of biscuits he had found whilst everyone was talking.

'I give up,' said Drake, 'what will we ever do with you Murphy, you're either being naughty or have your head in a prayer book.'

They all started laughing as Murphy slipped the empty biscuit box onto the table and got back onto his chair.

So the arrangements were made at the end of the week that they would all go to Foldingham and see the ship and wave Drake off as the ship sets sail. The puppies remembered the excitement the last time they went to the harbour that time in Drakeshead when there was a fairground and bands playing.

'It won't be quite like that this time,' Drake had warned, 'this time we shall set sail from Foldingham rather than Drakeshead which is a much bigger port and boats are coming and going all of the time not like here in Drakeshead where it is a rare thing. I want you all to come along though and see the boat leave and Jock can come along to help as well.'

The next few days at school the main topic of conversation was that The Admiral was going back to sea. The puppies started to realise how important The Admiral was and how everyone respected him, even Miss Primbling who was not given to showing any emotion seemed excited by the idea of an Admiral going to sea in a large sailing ship and that Admiral being the father of seven of her pupils.

'You puppies will have to tell us all about it next week when you return from Foldingham. We'll have one whole class set aside to hear your stories.'

This made the puppies feel very important. Mollie was still wary of some of the older pupils who she felt didn't like all the attention that was being lavished on these newcomers. She confided in Paddy her fears as usual but he tried to re-assure her and said he would be there to look after everyone, although he secretly shared her worries. Saturday came and they all piled into the 'big truck' with Drake driving and Pru in the front passenger seat. The two rows of seats behind were filled up with the seven puppies and Jock. Stubbings waved them off with a tearful look having made them a packed lunch for the journey. So they headed out of the village and up the mountain road. The puppies had almost forgotten this journey although the last time they went to Foldingham was to the carol service which turned out to be more eventful than expected. From the mountain road they could see the village laid out before them with The Hall and church, the village green, and what was even more exciting to the puppies they could see the school. All of them were leaning out to one side to look through the window to get a good view of the village which got smaller and smaller in the distance as they came over the top of the mountain road, and then they could see it no more.

It wasn't long on the other side before Mollie with her special vision could see Foldingham way off in the distance. She pointed from the back seat through the window.

'There's Foldingham cathedral in the distance.' No one else could see it yet.

'You must have very good eyes Moll,' said Drake from the front seat. 'I can't see it yet.'

'Our Mollie has got excellent eyesight,' said Pru, 'she always has had.'

It was a lot further on down the mountain before the others spotted Foldingham ahead of them and beyond that the harbour with the sea going off into the distance. They took the road on down and stopped halfway down the mountain at a parking area which had a perfect view of the county town of Foldingham, its cathedral and the harbour. They had their sandwiches and drinks which Stubbings had prepared.

Drake got out his binoculars and pointed out his boat in the harbour and they all took turns in looking through them to see the view. Murphy could not see anything through the glasses but then he was looking through them the wrong way around, which didn't surprise anyone.

Mollie could see way into the distance and could see other ships out at sea without the glasses but didn't point them out to anyone other than Paddy as the others wouldn't believe her. So they carried on down to the town and then the harbour. It was a while before the boat was due to sail but there was a lot of activity loading the cargo and provisions on board. All the sailors down at the quay recognised Drake and saluted him as he went on board. He spoke to the crew and checked all was going to plan and then he brought Pru and the puppies and Jock on board for a tour of the boat. He explained all about the crow's nest and how a sailor stayed on watch and warned of other ships or sightings of land ahead and how dangerous a job it was. As they turned away Pru spotted Murphy heading off on his own about to start climbing up towards the crow's nest.

'Don't even think about it Murphy!' she shouted and immediately he turned and joined the rest of the party.

'Just looking Mum, just looking,' he responded.

After the tour was over Drake took them all to the Admiral's cabin where they sat around the map table and he showed them where he was going to take the ship this time. The band was now playing outside and it would soon be time to cast off and set sail. One by one the puppies came and sat on his knee and said their goodbyes, none of them managing to hide their tears.

'I think it's best Jock if you take the puppies down onto the quay now and Pru and I will be down soon after you. I want you to take good care of everyone whilst I'm away. If there is any danger of me never returning from sea then you must look after them well Jock, and also look after Pru and Stubbings. Any sign by the way of your memory returning? Did we pass anything on the way today that you remember?'

'Not a thing,' said Jock 'I only remember a storm and a black and white cat. No more than that. The next thing I remember is your kindness to me and how that has continued and I will always be grateful.'

'Oh well,' said Drake, 'please help out with life at The Hall whilst I am away. I won't be long on this trip.'

Jock led the puppies off onto the quay whilst Pru and Drake said their farewells.

'You will be careful won't you Drake. The puppies and I need you home safely as soon as possible.'

'I will be careful my love,' said Drake, giving Pru a kiss. Drake led Pru onto the quay and said his final goodbyes. The boat was ready to leave, the band was playing rousing music and all the puppies had their flags to wave. Drake went back onto the ship and gave the command to set sail. The boat started slowly as it slid away and then picked up speed. Drake waved to them a final time and then went about his duties commanding the crew. Pru and the puppies watched as the boat slipped away getting ever smaller as it went into the distance. Soon it was just a speck on the horizon and then it was gone altogether. Mollie could still see it clearly and she confided to Paddy, but didn't share this fact with the others.

'Come along Jock let's get back to Drakeshead and get these puppies home for their tea,' said Pru.

Pru drove and Paddy and Mollie sat in the front seat and chatted all the way home. Jock and the others sat in the back and discussed the ship and the maps and where Dad was going to and when he would be back. In fact they never stopped until the truck pulled into the drive outside The Hall and they had got home before they even knew it. Nothing changes at The Hall, there was Stubbings waiting smoothing down her apron with lashings of fresh lemonade and cakes and biscuits waiting to greet them. What a welcome home.

CHAPTER THIRTEEN

TACHE'S ARRIVAL

After settling in to Stubbings' lavish tea, Pru told her they had all been on a tour of The Admiral's ship and had sat around the map table in The Admiral's cabin and afterwards had examined the charts. Although Foldingham was the county town, there was no fair at the harbour like there had been at Drakeshead, but the puppies had all waved off the ship as it had left, and brought their flags back to show her.

They thanked her for the tea, and were all about to think of having an early night when Stubbings said, 'By the way my Lady there is a black and white cat in the drawing room come to see you. He entered through the front door soon after you had left as bold as brass, said he was expected, and would wait by the fire for you. I thought he had a bit of a nerve but he gave me his card and said he was expected, so I put him in the drawing room.'

Stubbings fetched the card from the silver tray on the hall table and passed the card to Pru and she put her glasses on to make sense of the ornate black writing on the plain white card. It simply said in French, *Monsieur Tache*' and under that it said *Fils de Compte de Chat, Lille, France*.

'What did this cat look like Stubbings? Was he black and white with a black mark over the left side of his face?'

'Yes that's the very marking,' said Stubbings. 'He had a black cane with a silver top to it and he walked in a very aristocratic way.'

'I do believe this is the same cat that helped Jock. I think before I go into the drawing room and meet Monsieur Tache I will have a word with Jock and get him to come in with me.'

'I am not sure what The Admiral would think of all this,' said Stubbings. 'Highly irregular you know, he's not fond of cats at the best of times.'

'Leave it all to me,' said Pru. 'Where's Jock?' She soon found Mr Jock and showed him the visiting card.

'That sounds like the same cat that helped me when I was lost in the storm and I remember he did have a black cane with a silver handle which he lent to me to help me through the snow. May I come with you my Lady to the drawing room?'

So they entered the drawing room to see their new visitor sitting cross- legged by the fire, fast asleep snoring loudly.

'He certainly seems to have made himself comfortable,' said Pru.

At that point Tache woke with a start and stood to his feet, reached out, took Pru's paw, kissed it and said in his broken English accent, 'Your Ladyship I am delighted to meet you. I am Tache and I see you have looked after my friend, Mr Jock, very well. He looks fully recovered. I was passing by and felt you wouldn't mind me dropping in to see how Jock was.'

'No,' said Pru. 'You're most welcome,' she added not knowing what else to say. 'Poor Mr Jock has lost his memory, but all he talks about is the kindness shown to him by a black and white cat called Tache. Tell us about yourself Monsieur Tache, where are you from?'

'Originally I was from Lille in France, my father is the Compte de Chat, a very noble family of cats stretching back many generations and associated with the French Royal Family.'

Pru was impressed by these connections. 'What brings you to Drakeshead and this area?'

'I am a traveller your Ladyship, when my work is done in one place I move on and go where I can be of help again. My journeys have brought me this way, and the purpose will unfold before me. Now I have arrived here I would ask if I too may stay a while and continue to help my friend here Mr Jock and possibly help him regain his memory and also be of assistance to him in his duties.'

It was late and Pru was tired, she had found the evening's new arrival strange but could see no harm in finding him food and a bed for the night.

'Have you eaten Monsieur Tache?'

'No.'

'Well let's take you to the kitchen and get Stubbings to lay up supper for you. You met Stubbings on the way in I believe. We also have seven puppies who have gone to bed now and I will introduce you to them in the morning. There is a spare bed in Mr Jock's room you can have for tonight if that is OK. Is that OK with you Mr Jock?'

'Absolutely fine your Ladyship.'

As they headed off into the kitchen Pru turned to Tache, 'Remind me again where your name comes from, it's unusual what is the story?'

'Tache, your Ladyship is French for mark or spot as in the word moustache (meaning mark above the mouth). I was called Tache because of the distinct black mark to the left of my face and that has remained my name.'

'I like it,' said Pru. 'It is an aristocratic sounding name and of good lineage I do believe.'

She handed him over to Stubbings who made him supper and Jock showed him to his bed. Pru was exhausted and she made her way upstairs, firstly looking in on the puppies and then kissing each of them on the forehead. Finally she came to Paddy and Mollie's room at the front of the house. They were both wide awake.

'Who is the visitor?' asked Paddy.

'A French cat,' said Mollie. 'He is black and white with a mark on his face and he has a French accent.'

'You two don't miss anything do you, with your special

hearing Paddy and your special sight Mollie. We're going to have to make sure you're both trained to use these special senses and any other special powers that I don't know about. Monsieur Tache is a friend of Jock's, well let's say he helped Jock and although I don't know much about him, I think he came to do us some good. I have the same feelings that I had when Jock arrived, but I am not yet sure how they are going to help us, but I think the three of us will know more in the next day or two. Now sleep well my precious ones.'

Pru kissed Mollie and Paddy on the forehead. She turned off the light and then made her way to bed.

CHAPTER FOURTEEN

PADDY AND MOLLIE

The next morning all the puppies had heard of the new arrival at The Hall. Pru was down from breakfast early and told them that Jock would bring Monsieur Tache to breakfast and they could all meet him.There was no school today so they would have plenty of time to talk to him.

'You may have to listen very carefully as his English is with a French accent,' said Pru. Sure enough in about ten minutes Jock opened the door and led in Monsieur Tache who was taken around the table and introduced to each puppy in turn. With each introduction Tache made a bow and declared, 'Delighted to meet you young monsieur,' (or young mademoiselle as appropriate).

He was charming to all of them and once the introductions were over serious questioning began. Pru felt she would leave them to get on with it as they might be able to find out more than she had. Tache told them all about France, French life and the life of an aristocrat living in France. He told them of the customs of eating snails and frogs' legs and tried to teach them a few French words to practise. Between them the puppies chattered for most of the morning and Pru had to come and break up the party as Stubbings wanted to get on with preparing the lunch.

'You slept well Monsieur Tache?' asked Pru.

'Wonderfully, your Ladyship and I have had a good breakfast, but now I must work for my living and I propose to help Jock with his duties. We will work in the garden, bringing you wood for the fires and I will help Madame Stubbings to clean and polish. You tell me what to do and I will do it,' he said and with no further ado he and Jock were off to the garden cutting wood, stacking logs and gardening. Pru and Stubbings watched in amazement.

'Strange couple, your Ladyship, they work well together, I suspect that they have worked together before, your Ladyship, I think there is a bit more to them than meets the eye if you ask me.'

You may be right Stubbings, you may be right, thought Pru but said nothing aloud. She didn't know how Drake would have handled the situation if he had been home, probably better that he wasn't here at the moment.

That evening after the puppies had gone to bed, Pru sat up late by the fire on her own. Stubbings, Jock and Tache were all tired and had gone to bed early as Pru suggested that they all had an early night. Pru said she would lock up and check the fires before she went to bed herself. She got up from her chair in the drawing room and went over to the fireplace, checked the fire was all right for the night, and then turned out the lights and headed into the hallway.

There was her old pink chair. She had been so busy of late she hadn't had time to sit in it recently. She thought as she was passing by she would just rest for a while and the lights were now low in the hallway. There was a light over the picture of Moll Doggins who looked down at her reassuringly. The grandfather clock ticked away peacefully opposite. She looked towards the stairs and remembered the time she had come home and caught the puppies sliding down the banister rail and landing on an old bean bag at the bottom of the stairs. She yawned and felt tired and she looked up at the French windows halfway up the stairs.

She hadn't been out on her chair on any adventures for a long time, but she felt far too tired tonight. She started to close her eyes and was just nodding off to sleep when she was awoken as the grandfather clock started to strike. It didn't seem to be striking any particular number of times, and the hands were not on the hour, so it should have been silent but it continued to strike. She turned round and as she looked at it the painted dial changed from its normal scene of the four seasons and the whole clock face became a pure white Labrador looking down at her. She instantly knew that this was Albos.

Albos looked towards her and said, 'Thank you for taking care of Jock and Tache. As promised I have sent you help to bring up the puppies, but in particular to train Paddy and Mollie and make them realise how special their powers are and what they can use them for.' As if from nowhere Jock and Tache were standing in front of the clock and Albos continued to talk.

'Pru you took Jock in and looked after him although he was a stranger. He looked small but he is not what he seems to be. Jock is my faithful servant Methuselah who I have sent to teach Paddy and Mollie about their powers and to train them in how to use them.'

At this point Jock's tiny frame started to rise from the ground and grow upwards towering over Pru. His shape changed to that of a tall Chinese Waterhound dressed completely in white with a white beard and long flowing white moustache. Pru stared in amazement at the change that had occurred to Jock who now looked down at her and said, 'I am Methuselah,' in a deep voice, 'and each night I will change from Jock to my normal form as you see me now and I will train Paddy and Mollie.'

'Don't be afraid Pru,' said Albos still speaking from the clock face. 'Methuselah will train the puppies at night and they will continue to go to school by day with the others.'

'But what about their sleep?' asked Pru.

'The time that they spend with Methuselah will be as if the time has never passed,' said Albos reassuringly. 'They will spend all the hours of the night with him, but it will not appear as even one minute of time has passed by.'

Pru didn't really understand but trusted Albos. 'Where will all this take place, this training?' asked Pru.

Albos smiled back from the clock face, 'Methuselah will show you where it will all happen, it will take place in the White Room upstairs.'

'But we don't have a White Room,' said Pru.

'Oh yes you do,' said Albos. 'Methuselah will show you and the puppies.'

'And what of Tache?' asked Pru.

'Whilst Methuselah is teacher to Paddy and Mollie, my dear old friend Tache, who has been with me for as long as time exists, will stay with you as their guardian. Tache can follow Paddy and Mollie and keep watch over them, he is no ordinary cat, he can change shape and size and has powers to protect the growing puppies from any danger.'

At that point Tache towered up over Pru having shot up in size to be larger than a lion with great fangs of teeth and snarled in her direction and then shrank down to the size of a mouse and slipped through a crack in the base of the grandfather clock and vanished.

'You see Pru, these two, Tache and Methuselah, will work together to both protect and teach Paddy and Mollie. I will join you in a few moments,' said Albos speaking from the clock face.

Meanwhile Tache reappeared in his normal size. Methuselah had quietly slipped back to being Jock.

'The three of you,' said Albos, 'make your way up to the puppies' bedroom and I will join you later.'

Pru shook her head from side to side. Was this a dream?

Jock and Tache led the way and Pru followed as they headed up to the front bedroom where Paddy and Mollie slept. It was late and Pru didn't like waking them but she had no option. They were awake anyway when she went into the room and were sitting up in their beds. Pru sat on one of the beds and said she had some surprises for them. There was no need they knew anyway.

'We had a dream Mum,' said Mollie.

'We each had the same dream,' said Paddy, 'that just woke us up. We dreamt that Jock became a tall Chinese teacher in a long white robe called Methuselah who taught us every night in a big white room, and that Monsieur Tache protected us wherever we went and can change shape and be bigger than a lion and roar loudly, or become as small as a mouse.'

Pru smiled and said, 'I know this dream and it's true.'

They watched Jock change in front of them into Methuselah who then stood over them, 'Don't be afraid Paddy and Mollie.' He held Mollie's hand and for that moment all her fears she ever had just slipped away.

'All three of you come with me and Tache will follow. We have someone to meet who is very important and we must go to the White Room right away.'

'Where is this White Room?' asked Pru.

'It's through this wall here,' said Methuselah pointing to his left hand side.

'But there is no room there,' said Pru.

'There has always been a room Pru but you have never known it. Now the puppies must hold each other's paws and you Mollie hold my paw.' Methuselah took Pru's paw with his other paw on the other side and they stepped forwards. 'Don't be afraid,' he said, 'just believe and hold onto me. Tache will follow us.'

They stepped forward and Pru had her eyes tightly closed thinking she would be knocked out by the hard stone wall, but guided by Methuselah they stepped through the wall and into the White Room beyond. Afterwards Tache stepped in with his silver handled black cane and simply passed through the wall joining the others in the White Room.

CHAPTER FIFTEEN

THE WHITE ROOM

Pru stood with Mollie and Paddy looking around the vast, pure white room that they found themselves in. The ceiling was supported by white marble pillars with huge Labradors at the top of them taking the weight of the ceiling. Down either side of the room were white double doors under archways with names written over the doors.

For a moment Pru and Paddy and Mollie just stood and looked around. The room was bigger than anything they could imagine and everything was pure white. They looked around the room again and could see there were at least three large doors down each side of the room and one at each end. None of the group could make out what the writing was over the doors, but as they looked further into the distance at the end of the room, there sitting on a pure white throne sat Albos himself.

He smiled towards the group and beckoned to Pru and said, 'Bring Mollie and Paddy forward so that I can see them.'

Pru led the group forward feeling less afraid herself now and as she approached the throne she turned to Paddy and Mollie and said to them, 'Now don't be afraid either of you, this is Albos.'

The puppies just stared up in amazement. Methuselah and Tache had accompanied them and stood either side of the group and Tache was walking in his usual swanky way with his black cane with the silver handle. They both smiled proudly as they looked up at Albos.

Albos sat and just spent some time looking at both of the puppies in front of him as this was the first time they had met. He then stepped down from the throne, his white robe flowing behind him. He sat himself down on the steps of the throne so that he was the same height as Mollie and Paddy.

He looked at both of them and then said, 'You two are both very special, I have watched you growing up and seen how your powers are already developing.' He turned to Mollie, 'You, little Mollie, have very special powers of sight and can see into the distance and through solid objects. Remember when you saw the chandelier in the cathedral in the darkness when it started to fall, and again how you continued to be able to see your father's boat out at sea long after everyone else had lost sight of it. You may remember you couldn't see inside the snowman at Christmas but that was different, they were very special magic presents that Moll Doggins had put in the snowman for you, so don't be alarmed or be afraid that you were unable to see these as she did not want you to know what you were having or what the others were getting. I know you have always been afraid but Paddy will be with you to support you and Methuselah will help you to learn how to feel strong and brave.'

Albos then turned to Paddy, who was also very white for a Labrador but not the pure colour that Albos was, but seeing them together there was a close similarity. Albos put his paws around Paddy's head and looked into Paddy's eyes, 'You my boy are going to be very strong and brave, you already know you have special powers of hearing, don't you? Back in the cathedral that time you could hear the chandelier creaking before it fell and you rushed out and saved Bishop Rodney. I was proud of you both that night and your actions in saving The Bishop.'

Albos then turned to Pru who was standing just behind the other two and said, 'You are bringing them up well, Pru, and also their brothers and sisters, well done.'

Albos stepped back up the two little steps and took his place back on the throne. He reached out with his paws pointing to the room they were in. The little band in front of him were spellbound by his actions. All were silent and then he spoke again.

'Let me introduce you to the White Room you didn't know this room existed did you Pru?'

'How can it exist?' asked Pru, 'as there is nothing on the outside wall of The Hall just trees.'

Albos looked down at Pru. 'You must realise, Pru, that just because you can't see something it doesn't mean it's not there. I believe that from the first time we met you have trusted what I tell you. Some things cannot be explained, they have to be believed, and here we are in this room. Walk over to the walls and touch them, touch the floor.' Pru then obediently touched the floor. 'Yes you see it's all pure white marble, surely it all exists,' said Albos.

Pru nodded not sure where they were but knew she had to trust Albos. Sure enough the floor felt solid. Albos sat back in his throne with his elbows resting on the arms of the great chair. He looked around at the five of them in front of him and smiled. Turning to Pru, Paddy and Mollie he pointed with his right paw to Methuselah who stood very tall and looked very serious.

'Methuselah has been with me since time began and was with my father before me. He has trained all the generations of Goddogs and he will now train Mollie and Paddy how to use their special powers. He will teach you every night here in The White Room. You will still go to school by day but here every night you will learn all about the world, its history and geography and you will learn how to be experts in mathematics and reading and writing. You will be taught about music and how to paint and how to become physically fit. You will learn how to do everything you will need to be able to do so that when you are grown up you will be able to use your special powers to good and help others in need.'

Albos looked at Mollie and Paddy while he talked and

marvelled at how quiet and good they were while they listened to everything he said.

'I want you to grow up normally with your brothers and sisters who will never know anything of this, you will go to school by day and learn and play with the others, but your real teaching will be with Methuselah at night here in The White Room.'

Turning to Monsieur Tache, Albos pointed with his paw, 'He will protect you, he can go anywhere and can change shape to be smaller than a pin head or be larger than a mighty roaring lion. He will watch over you, so you see little Mollie, with Paddy at your side and Monsieur Tache watching over you, yes you really have nothing to fear.'

'So,' said Albos, 'I need to show you around the White Room so that you can see what is in store for you.'

He then stepped down from the throne again and led the little group over to the left hand side of the room. 'You will see there are three large double doors on this wall under marble arches. Over the doors you will read what you will find when you go through them. On the left hand side of the White Room are the rooms where you will learn about mathematics and spelling and foreign languages.'

Mollie looked very sad at the thought, 'It doesn't sound like much fun,' she said to Paddy very quietly thinking that only he could hear.

'Oh I think you'll find all this is a lot of fun my little Mollie,' said Albos.

Mollie was quite shocked to think that he had heard as she had only whispered but she was beginning to realise what powers Albos had.

'Down the right wall of the hall are doorways leading to rooms where you will learn of history and science, together with the arts including painting and sculpture and music.' Albos swung around pointing to the rooms on the right. 'Shall

I take you for a tour around the rooms so I can show you what's in through the doors?'

He turned to Paddy, 'I can see that you're thinking what are the doors at either end of the hall. Well you'll have to continue thinking until we have looked into the other rooms. Let's go to the left hand side first.' They went over all together to the first door on the left. The marble arch over the door had written on it *Mathematics*.

Mollie and Paddy looked at each other horrified, they had only just started school and they already dreaded the thought of mathematics. All those tables and sums, it all seemed such hard work and it was so boring.

'I know what you're thinking,' said Albos reading their minds, 'but I can assure you this will all be different than going to school.'

Methuselah and Tache opened the doors and they walked into the room to find they were in a garden full of trees with birds singing beautiful songs. They all followed Albos into the garden. The trees seemed to go on for ever and ever into the distance and there were sweet smelling flowers around them.

'It doesn't seem much like a mathematics lesson,' Paddy whispered to Mollie.

'I hear what you're saying,' said Albos, 'but just watch this. What's 4+4,' he said in a loud voice and at this point two white doves flew down from the blossom trees. Each one had a 4 on its chest as they flew up close to Paddy and Mollie and then hovered in front of them.

The first one said, 'I am a 4,' and the second dove said, 'I am a 4 also,' and then they flew closer and closer and flapped their wings so fast the puppies could not see them apart. Then the next thing they knew there was only one white dove in front of them and this dove had an 8 on its chest. It turned its head from side to side looking at Mollie and Paddy and it said to them, 'You see, 4+4 equals 8,' and then it flew back up into the trees.

'Mathematics can be fun,' said Albos. 'In this garden you will discover that and all the birds are here to help you.' At this point there was a whole flurry of activity in the trees and the air above was full of birds flying in all directions and then a large owl flew down and landed on Albos' paw which he held up to receive him.

'This, my little friends, is Euclyd. He is in charge here in the garden and he will keep all the other birds in order.'

Euclyd bowed to Albos and then turned to Methuselah and bowed.

'It's good to see you again, it's been a long time and we are all ready to teach these puppies all that we know.' Euclyd turned to Paddy and Mollie, 'I think you'll enjoy your time here with us learning about numbers and mathematics and I will look forward to teaching you.'

Neither Paddy nor Mollie had seen an owl before let alone one who was a mathematics teacher but they had already gone passed being surprised by anything. Euclyd took a bow and flew off into the woods. The nightingales were singing and night was now falling. The little group turned to leave and they thought long and hard about the future and the lessons they would enjoy in their mathematics schoolroom.

As they left the birds sang loudly and Methuselah and Tache closed the double doors and then the sound was gone.

'It seems a strange sort of maths class,' Paddy whispered to Mollie.

'I thought it was lovely in there Paddy, well worth learning mathematics if it means we can go back in there again,' said Mollie.

'Where shall we go next?' asked Albos. 'Shall we go left or right?' He pointed in either direction. 'Mollie, what about you choosing which way. To the right we have "history and geography" and to the left we have languages.'

'Oh I don't want to know about languages yet,' said Mollie,

'can we go and look at history?'

So they went to the room with *History* written over the door and again the doors were flung open by Tache and Methuselah and they went on in. They were surprised when they went through the doors to find themselves on the quay in Foldingham with sailing ships in the harbour and there stepping off the boat in full costume was a seafaring dog from days gone by. It was a costume that they had only seen pictures of that their father had shown them in old sailing books. A sea captain stepped forward and saluted Albos and Methuselah and greeted the others.

'Paddy, Mollie,' said Albos, 'meet Captain Scrimshot. He'll teach you all about history and geography Now today we find ourselves in the year 1700 just name a year and a place and the Captain will take you there on his ship and you will learn all about those times and places. In years to come you will also find this room will have other uses but we'll tell you about that in the future.'

'Can we go back and see Moll Doggins and really meet a Squirmit,' said Mollie surprised at herself asking such a question. She had always been petrified at the thought of meeting a Squirmit, but today was different, she seemed to have no fears of such things.

Albos turned to her, 'Not here my little Mollie, but later I will show you how you can learn all about your own past and see Moll Doggins and we may get a peep at the odd Squirmit, but that may be for another time.'

'So that's history and geography and Captain Scrimshot will look after you for all your lessons here.'

Captain Scrimshot got back on his boat and bade them farewell and said he would see them in the future and Albos led them back into the main hallway.

'Let's move on up to the languages room.' Tache had already gone ahead of the group and was opening the doors for them.

He had gone inside and greeted them with 'welcome, *bien venue*, *wilcommen, croeso,*" reading off endless greetings in different languages. Behind him stretched out into the distance a landscape which changed as he spoke a different language. There were road signs and menus which changed from English to French and then into Italian and then Welsh depending on the language which Tache spoke in.

'How does it all happen like this?' asked Paddy surprised at what was occurring before his eyes.

'Paddy I thought by now that you had realised that you should accept that anything is possible,' said Albos.

Pru sighed, 'I gave up being surprised years ago and learnt to accept whatever occurs.'

'Tache is in charge of languages and you have seen him change from one language to another. You have seen him change in shape and he can also talk in any language and show you about the customs and ways of different countries.'

Tache stepped forward and ran through a whole selection of different greetings again and the puppies were amazed at how the landscape kept changing from country to country with different wording on the signs.

'Enough of the different languages,' said Albos. 'Let's show them something else Tache.'

Tache took Mollie and Paddy by their paws and led them over to a large well in the middle of a courtyard in the language room.

'This is the Spelling Well, any word you need to know how to spell can be found in this well. There isn't a word that is known that is not in here.'

Paddy and Mollie looked into the dark waters of the well wondering what Tache was talking about.

Pru stepped over and looked in, 'It looks just like a well full of water to me,' she sighed.

Albos was smiling. 'You'll enjoy the Spelling Well and learn a lot from it Paddy and Mollie. Would you like a demonstration?'

Methuselah stepped forwards, 'Mollie give me a word,' he said.

Mollie thought for a moment, 'What about Squirmit,' she said pleased with herself for thinking of a long word.

'That's fine,' said Methuselah. He turned towards the well and said,' Spelling Well, spell Squirmit please.' At this point the still waters started to bubble and suddenly eight letters rose up to the surface and formed a circle on the water and moved around and jumbled up together and then settled on the surface, which had now become still, and the letters spelt out SQUIRMIT in clear bold letters.

Mollie was so excited at this her tail was wagging frantically, 'How does it work, how does it work? I could stay and play learning to spell at the well all day.'

Methuselah turned back to the waters and said, 'Thank you,' and the letters vanished back below the water level.

'I thought you would like the Spelling Well,' said Albos. 'Methuselah will bring you back here in due course.' Albos turned to the group again and said, 'We must move on and look at the rooms on the other side of the great hall.'

The first room had *The Arts* written over the door. Methuselah opened the door which led into a vast gallery with sculptures down the centre and pictures on the wall, going off into the distance further than they could see. There appeared to be a mist in the distance in the room which was so long they could not see the far end, and there were other galleries going off from both walls as they walked along.

'In this room I will show you all the art of the world,' said Methuselah, proudly pointing to the sculptures and various paintings on the wall. 'I will show you how to paint and to make sculptures yourselves, perhaps not as good as some of these but we'll have fun trying. When we've learnt all about these we'll move on and teach you about music, which is in the next room.'

Pru couldn't believe that all these pictures and sculptures could be here in this room which she didn't even know existed. They moved onto the next room.

'I think you'd better be prepared for this room,' said Albos, 'it was always one of my favourites when I was small. I suggest Paddy, Mollie and Pru you cover up your eyes whilst Methuselah and Tache open the doors.'

The doors were opened and there was the sound of an orchestra playing music, the trumpeters playing a fanfare and drum rolls, violins and every form of instrument could be heard.

'The music is wonderful,' said Pru 'where is it coming from?'

'Uncover your eyes now and step forwards,' said Albos and as they entered they found themselves in a vast concert hall with an orchestra consisting of different Poodles all in evening dress playing instruments. There were three very large black Poodles in bow ties on the drums and rows of miniature poodles on the violins to the left of the conductor. The conductor was a fairly chubby Schnauzer with hair flying around in all directions as he waved his baton furiously, the tails on his jacket flying around behind him.

'I always felt this was a wonderful room,' said Albos, 'you see they can play any music and Methuselah will teach you all about it.'

'Can they play all music?' asked Mollie. 'Could they even play our song we used to sing when we were frightened there might a Squirmit about?'

Pru looked quite sternly at her, 'Don't be silly Mollie, that is a long time ago when we used to sing that song it was when you were very tiny.'

'It's OK,' Albos said. 'I am sure it is possible.' He turned to the orchestra waved his paw at them and said a few words, at which point a choir arose behind the orchestra and the music played in the background to the little rap song that the puppies had sung when they were very young and heard the story about the Squirmits: 'You'd better watch out there's a Squirmit about.'

Albos watched and laughed loudly. 'You see Pru, anything is possible.'

When the little rap song was finished the choir disappeared and the orchestra went back to playing some quiet music in the background.

'Let's move on,' said Albos and the doors were closed and the sound of the orchestra was gone.

'Enough of all this learning,' said Albos, 'the last room is the gymnasium.'

They looked up and over the door there this was written: *Gymnasium.* 'This is where you can exercise and you can become strong Paddy and learn to run fast,' said Albos.

'I'm not good at running,' said Mollie and felt worried about this room.

'Don't worry Mollie,' said Albos, 'Methuselah will teach you how to use your special powers so you will not need to learn everything that Paddy has to know, but I think you'll enjoy this room.'

The doors were flung open and in front of them there was a running track with exercise machines and in the distance playing fields going off as far as they could see. To the right hand side was a balcony and Albos led them on to this.

'Take a seat all of you.' In front of them stretched out was a cricket match being played on the village green next to a church. Two tall Retrievers were batting and a very fast Spaniel was bowling.

'Let's sit and watch the cricket for a few moments,' said Albos, as a Dalmatian in tails and bow tie stepped forward.

At that moment the church clock beside the village green

struck four o'clock The Dalmatian turned to Albos and said, 'Tea sir.' He carried a tray and put it on the table to the side of Albos and served them tea and cucumber sandwiches and cake. He wore white gloves as he served them all, passing the tea around on a silver tray. Albos turned to Pru and with a smile said, 'You see, your Ladyship, standards have to be maintained.'

She smiled back at Albos and raised her cup to him, 'Excellent tea and the best cucumber sandwiches I have ever tasted.' After they had eaten tea they sat and watched a little cricket and then they left the gymnasium room and were all back in the main hallway.

'These are the rooms where Methuselah, Tache and their friends will teach you,' Albos said to Mollie and Paddy. 'I think you are impressed.'

They just looked back up at him and nodded, rather lost for words. Paddy found his voice first, 'Excuse me but where do we learn how to make rockets and repair tractors, and all those exciting things?'

Albos bent down on one knee and said to him, 'Ah my little friend you've noticed, no science, no mechanics, no computers, there are lots of things missing aren't there? Well. I've only shown you six rooms today and there are many more rooms that you can't see but will be taken to in the future. Don't worry you'll learn how to mend you tractor and you will learn how to make a rocket and to learn all about computers, but that's all for another time.' Albos stood up and pointed again, 'You will have noticed at each end of the great hall are two other doorways, the one behind you is call *The Past* and that room Mollie and Paddy is where you will learn of your own past, where you will meet Moll Doggins one day, and possibly even a Squirmit if they exist.'

Mollie looked very excited at this but Albos held up his paw and looked quite stern as he said, 'But not now we will have to leave this room for the moment.'

'What does the last room contain, the one right over in the distance behind your throne?' Paddy asked feeling very bold now.

'That room is your future,' said Albos, 'and not even Methuselah or Tache can enter that room, only I, Albos can enter. The door will remain locked at all times, but I can assure you I will make sure that your future is safe and I will always protect you both. Enough now, I must leave you all. Methuselah and Tache will take you back and you must get some sleep. Goodbye Pru and well done. Goodbye Mollie, goodbye Paddy, we will all meet again soon in the future.' Albos walked back to his throne, sat on the throne and waved to them. As he spoke swirling mists came around the throne and the doors to the room which he said held the future opened and the chair went backwards in the mist, and the doors closed behind him.

Pru turned to her puppies and bent down to talk to them, 'We have all learnt many things tonight and you have both been so good. Only we three can share what we know, but we have Methuselah here to help us and Tache to protect us.'

Methuselah said, 'It's time now my Lady that we were returning. Paddy, hold on to Mollie's paw and I will take your paw and you hold my paw on this side Pru,' and they stepped forward and went through the wall again and found themselves back in Paddy and Mollie's bedroom. Tache picked up his silver handled stick, looked around the White Room and strode forwards passing through the wall. Pru took Mollie and Paddy back into their beds, kissed them on their foreheads.

'Look at them they are so tired,' she said turning to Methuselah who had already changed back to being Jock, with Tache standing next to him. The two little ones were soon fast asleep snoring loudly.

'I think it's time your Ladyship got some rest,' said Jock. 'Tache and I will check the house is secure.'

So Pru headed off to bed. She thought what a night it had been and how things had always been at The Hall and worried how they could ever be the same again after this night, and then she was asleep.

CHAPTER SIXTEEN

PRU'S BIRTHDAY

Pru sat in her old chair in the hallway, it was the morning of her birthday and the post was piled up on the silver tray on the hall table next to her. There were all the cards from the family and soon she would start to open them and lay them out for everyone to see when they arrived for lunch.

She looked up at the painting of Moll Doggins on the wall and thought to herself how the years had been kind to her, living here at The Hall, having a fine husband like Drake and her crowning glory, her seven puppies. Of course she loved them all dearly, but it had never been a secret that she had a special place in her heart for Paddy and Mollie. How could it have ever been any other way. They were the two special ones with special powers. None of the others knew this, and she had never even been able to share her knowledge with Drake, those powers which they now used for good and to help others and fight evil in the world. She sat back and thought what adventures she had had in this pink chair in the early days before the puppies and later the mysteries that she had learnt, firstly from Albos and then from Methuselah. She smiled to herself and thought of that French black and white cat Monsieur Tache and how well he had looked after Paddy and Mollie through the years. I wonder whatever became of him, she thought. One day he had just gone never to be seen again.

She thought back to that night when they first visited the White Room. To this day she can't understand where that room is and yet off the main hall in the White Room she learnt how it was possible to visit far off lands and go back and learn about history. How much Paddy and Mollie learnt through those years and yet every day they went off to school with the other brothers and sister and nobody knew about all these things that she had had to keep to herself through the years.

Pru looked up at the grandfather clock. It was eleven o'clock and she expected the family at around twelve noon for lunch. Enough of the past for now she thought, we can return to that later, I had better open up these cards and get myself ready for their arrival. Standards mustn't be seen to be slipping at The Hall and I need to be looking my best as I have a little surprise for the family.

She reached over the silver salver and took the pile of cards. One by one she opened them. The first was from PC Bramley, she knew this would be a fairly serious card and she wasn't mistaken. She knew he meant well and put it to one side. The next was obviously from Bentley, he was the artistic one and always painted his own cards. As usual this was the case, no doubt he would appear at lunchtime carrying an enormous display of flowers – they got more outrageous each year but they were wonderful. Next one and surprise surprise a it was golfing scene from Nicole who was always dancing, dancing, dancing but these days the golf seems to have taken over. As usual, a small card from The Reverend Murphy with a slightly religious verse and from her Tebor a very clever card she thought as he had taken a photo of Pru sitting in PRU 1, her beloved green Mercedes convertible with the roof down. That wretched roof she thought, it had caused her trouble all through the summer, either the boys must fix it or it would have to go.

There were only two left but she only expected one card as for years Paddy and Mollie had sent one card between them. She knew it would be very special and she opened the large gold envelope. She saw that on the front of the card was a picture of Paddy looking splendid in a white evening suit and a black bow tie. Mollie was sitting in a dashing red dress. Pru examined the card and thought how fine they both looked. Suddenly the picture started to come alive and both Paddy and

Mollie said together, 'Hi Mum, Happy Birthday to you.'

Pru put the card on the hall table and as she did so Paddy stepped out onto the table and Mollie stood up and stepped out also. They carried a miniature bunch of fifty red roses and laid these on the hall table. They then turned and sang perfectly Happy Birthday to her. She felt herself wanting to cry, but instead said, 'You two, what tricks will you think of next,' and laughed as the two of them stepped back into the card. Mollie took her seat and Paddy stood next to her and once again they were quite still.

The tiny bunch of roses on the hall table started to grow and grow until it reached normal size and there in front of Pru were fifty full red roses. Every year they thought of a different way to surprise her, but only the two of them and Pru knew these things and to anyone else in the family it was just a birthday card with a picture on it and it was just an ordinary bunch of flowers.

Pru smiled and laughed aloud to herself. She looked up at Moll Doggins who smiled back at her and she noticed the time. Goodness she must get a move on. It was time to change, now where were her best pearls, and yes she thought, her favourite tweed suit. She had to look her best today.

Drake was having a snooze before lunch and he was going to wear his full Admiral's uniform. He didn't go to sea so much these days but she still loved to see him in his naval outfit. What was it, she thought about uniforms that they were so smart, and then she remembered little Murphy in his uniform all those years ago going to school, shoe laces always undone, shirt tail hanging out. Well there's always an exception to the rule she thought, he could never have been described as smart in those days.

As Pru came down the stairs wearing her finest clothes and having her best pearls around her neck, Drake followed her down looking splendid dressed as first Admiral of the Fleet. He handed Pru his card and wished her a Happy Birthday. They didn't bother much with presents these days. Pru read her card and inside it said: 'With fondest love to my dearest Pru, a wonderful wife and mother.' Pru wiped a tear away from her eye.

'Well, come on my dear,' said Drake, 'what surprises have you lined up for the family this year?'

'Come with me,' said Pru taking Drake's right paw and opening the front door there was a large gold chair placed at the bottom of the steps outside The Hall and opposite it was a photographer waiting to take the family photograph.

'I have told everyone to get here as quickly as they can, I am going to sit in the chair,' said Pru taking her place, 'and you Drake stand to my left holding the back of the chair.'

Next to arrive were Bentley, Bramley and Tebor, they still kept very close even after all these years and had met in "The Two Collies" for a drink before arriving. None of the puppies knew of the picture and hadn't dressed up specially which is how Pru had wanted it. She had given instructions to just come along from work for a spot of lunch – nothing special. Tebor was in his brown overalls still and had the odd screwdriver sticking out from various pockets. PC Bramley was, well, PC Bramley in his policeman's outfit, Bentley was as expected carrying a huge creation of exotic flowers and was wearing a colourful waistcoat and bright pink tie. Pru wondered about his colour scheme sometimes, but only Bentley could carry off such a mixture of colours.

Then almost dancing up the drive came Nicole, golf club still in hand. She kissed her mother and wished her a Happy Birthday and was given her place to stand between her father and her three brothers for the picture. Next, prayer book in hand, The Reverend Murphy wearing his dog collar and black suit came up the drive. He likewise kissed his mother and made a small but notable sign of the cross.

Pru beckoned him to stand to her right, but to leave room for Paddy and Mollie next to her. The two of them came up the drive together, Mollie straight from the surgery with her white coat on and a stethoscope around her neck. Next came Paddy in his tweed country suit with plus four trousers and in his working boots, having been working on the farm right up until a few minutes ago. They both apologised for being late and kissed Pru, who very quietly thanked them for their special card and flowers and told them how amused she had been by the card. She showed them their places to stand next to her and when everything was ready with a wave of her right paw to the photographer, the picture was ready to take.

They were all told to smile for the picture which everyone did, except for Pru who never allowed herself to be photographed with a smile. Standards must be maintained she always said. There was a large flash and the photograph was taken. At that point The Hall door opened and Stubbings appeared, 'Lunch is served your Ladyship,' she said and Pru led the party in to celebrate her birthday because that's the way things were always done at The Hall and that's the way they always would be.